W9-CRT-484

CHOICE   FEB. '7

Physics

CUNYNGHAME, Sir Henry Hardinge Samuel. Time and clocks; a description of ancient and modern methods of measuring time. Singing Tree Press, a div. of Gale, 1970 (orig. pub. by Archibald Constable & Co., 1906). 200p il 77-78127. 7.00

An incredible little book. It is an unaltered reprint of the 1906 edition. There is nothing really like it of more recent vintage. Cunynghame was most certainly a man of uncommon technical and historical competence. His phrases have at once beautiful simplicity and profound clarity. He was most assuredly a humanist. Here is enchanting reading wherein we learn about gravity; "A flea on this earth can skip perhaps eight inches high; put that flea on the moon, and with the expenditure of the same energy he could skip four feet high"; primitive ideas on time-keeping; sundials; water clocks; relativity of motion; springs; harmonic motion; pendulums; and finally the highly intricate mechanical devices of balance wheels, escapements and such. The text closes with: "May I end with a word of advice to parents?", revealing the author as a moralist of first rank. Good for young and old — schooled and unschooled. A splendid thing for collateral reading in every class. Abundantly illustrated with old fashioned sketches.

TIME AND CLOCKS:

*A DESCRIPTION OF ANCIENT
AND MODERN METHODS OF
MEASURING TIME.*

BY

H. H. CUNYNGHAME M.A. C.B. M.I.E.E.

WITH MANY ILLUSTRATIONS.

DETROIT
Singing Tree Press
1970

This is an unaltered reprint of the 1906
edition first published in London by
Archibald Constable & Co. Ltd.

Library of Congress Catalog Card Number: 77-78127

NUREMBERG CLOCK. CONVERTED FROM A VERGE ESCAPEMENT
TO A PENDULUM MOVEMENT.

TIME AND CLOCKS.

CONTENTS.

is necessary for the formation of society. During another, the study of the principles of morality and religion will be in the ascendant. During another the arts will take the lead ; during another, poetry, tragedy, and lyric poetry and prose will be cultivated ; during another, music will take its turn, and out of rude peasant songs will evolve the harmony of the opera.

To our age is reserved the glory of being easily the foremost in scientific discovery. Future ages may despise our literature, surpass us in poetry, complain that in philosophy we have done nothing, and even deride and forget our music ; but they will only be able to look back with admiration on the band of scientific thinkers who in the seventeenth century reduced to a system the laws that govern the motions of worlds no less than those of atoms, and who in the eighteenth and nineteenth founded the sciences of chemistry, electricity, sound, heat, light, and who gave to mankind the steam-engine, the telegraph, railways, the methods of making huge structures of iron, the dynamo, the telephone, and the thousand applications of science to the service of man.

And future students of history who shall be familiar with the conditions of our life will, I think, be also struck with surprise at our estimate of our own peculiar capabilities and faculties. They will note with astonishment that a gentleman of the

TIME AND CLOCKS.

INTRODUCTION.

WHEN we read the works of Homer, or Virgil, or Plato, or turn to the later productions of Dante, of Shakespeare, of Milton, and the host of writers and poets who have done so much to instruct and amuse us, and to make our lives good and agreeable, we are apt to look with some disappointment upon present times. And when we turn to the field of art and compare Greek statues and Gothic or Renaissance architecture with our modern efforts, we must feel bound to admit our inferiority to our ancestors. And this leads us perhaps to question whether our age is the equal of those which have gone before, or whether the human intellect is not on the decline.

This feeling, however, proceeds from a failure to remember that each age of the world has its peculiar points of strength, as well as of weakness. During one period that self-denying patriotism and zeal for the common good will be developing, which

nineteenth century, an age mighty in science, and
by no means pre-eminent in art, literature and
philosophy, should have considered it disgraceful
to be ignorant of the accent with which a Greek or
a Roman thought fit to pronounce a word, should
have been ashamed to be unable to construe a
Latin aphorism, and yet should have considered
it no shame at all not to know how a telephone was
made and why it worked. They will smile when
they observe that our highest university degrees, our
most lucrative rewards, were given for the study
of dead languages or archæological investigations,
and that science, our glory and that for which we
have shown real ability, should only have occupied
a secondary place in our education.

They will smile when they learn that we
considered that a knowledge of public affairs could
only be acquired by a grounding in Greek particles,
or that it could ever have been thought that men
could not command an army without a study of the
tactics employed at the battle of Marathon.

But the battle between classical and scientific
education is not in reality so much a dispute
regarding subjects to be taught, as between
methods of teaching. It is possible to teach classics
so that they become a mental training of the
highest value. It is possible to teach science so
that it becomes a mere enslaving routine.

The one great requirement for the education

of the future is firmly to grasp the fact that a study of words is not a study of things, and that a man cannot become a carpenter merely by learning the names of his tools.

It was the mistake of the teachers of the Middle Ages to believe that the first step in knowledge was to get a correct set of concepts of all things, and then to deduce or bring out all knowledge from them. Admirable plan if you can get your concepts ! But unfortunately concepts do not exist ready made—they must be grown; and as your knowledge increases, so do your concepts change. A concept of a thing is not a mere definition, it is a complete history of it. And you must build up your edifice of scientific knowledge from the earth, brick by brick and stone by stone. There is no magic process by which it can with a word be conjured into existence like a palace in the Arabian Nights.

For nothing is more fatal than a juggle with words such as force, weight, attraction, mass, time, space, capacity, or gravity. Words are like purses, they contain only as much money as you put into them. You may jingle your bag of pennies till they sound like sovereigns, but when you come to pay your bills the difference is soon discovered.

This fatal practice of learning words without trying to obtain a clear comprehension of their meaning, causes many teachers to use mathematical formulæ not as mere steps in a logical chain, but like magical chaldrons into which they put the premises as the witches put herbs and babies' thumbs into their pots, and expect the answers to rise like apparitions by some occult process that they cannot explain. This tendency is encouraged by foolish parents who like to see their infant prodigies appear to understand things too hard for themselves, and look on at their children's lessons in mathematics like rustics gaping at a fair. They forget that for the practical purposes of life one thing well understood is worth a whole book-full of muddled ill-digested formulæ. Unfortunately it is possible to cram boys up and run them through the examination sieves with the appearance of knowledge without its reality. If it were cricket or golf that were being tested how soon would the fraud be discovered. No humbug would be permitted in those interesting and absorbing subjects. And really, when one reflects how easy it is to present the appearance of book knowledge without the reality, one can hardly blame those who select men for service in India and Egypt a good deal for their proficiency in sports and games. Better a good cricketer than a silly pedant stuffed full of learning that " lies like marl upon a barren soil encumbering what is not in its power to fertilize."

Another kindred error is to expect too much of science. For with all our efforts to obtain a further knowledge of the mysteries of nature, we are only like travellers in a forest. The deeper we penetrate it, the darker becomes the shade. For science is " but an exchange of ignorance for that which is another kind of ignorance "* and all our analysis of incomprehensible things leads us only to things more incomprehensible still.

It is, therefore, by the firm resolution never to juggle with words or ideas, or to try and persuade ourselves or others that we understand what we do not understand, that any scientific advance can be made.

* *Manfred*, Act II., scene iv.

CHAPTER I.

ALL students of any subject are at first apt to be perplexed with the number and complication of the new ideas presented to them.

The need of comprehending these ideas is felt, and yet they are difficult to grasp and to define. Thus, for instance, we are all apt to think we know what is meant when force, weight, length, capacity, motion, rest, size, are spoken of. And yet when we come to examine.these ideas more closely, we find that we know very little about them. Indeed, the more elementary they are, the less we are able to understand them.

The most primordial of our ideas seem to be those of number and quantity; we can count things, and we can measure them, or compare them with one another. Arithmetic is the science which deals with the numbers of things and enables us to multiply and divide them. The estimation of quantities is made by the application of our faculty of comparison to different subjects. The ideas of number and quantity appear to pervade all our conceptions.

The study of natural phenomena of the world around us is called the study of physics from the

Greek word φνσίς or " inanimate nature," the
term physics is usually confined to such part of
nature as is not alive.   The study of living things
is usually termed biology (from βια, life).

In the study of natural phenomena there are,
however, three ideas which occupy a peculiar and
important position, because they may be used as
the means of measuring or estimating all the rest.
In this sense they seem to be the most primitive
and fundamental that we possess.   We are not
entitled to say that all other ideas are formed from
and compounded of these ideas, but we are entitled
to say that our correct understanding of physics,
that is of the study of nature, depends in no slight
degree upon our clear understanding of them.   The
three fundamental ideas are those of space, time
and mass.

Space appears to be the universal accompaniment
of all our impressions of the world around us.   Try
as we may, we cannot think of material bodies
except in space, and occupying space.   Though we
can imagine space as empty we cannot conceive it
as destroyed.   And this space has three dimensions,
length, breadth measured across or at right angles
to length, and thickness measured at right angles
to length and breadth.   More dimensions than this
we cannot have.   For some inscrutable reason it
has been arranged that space shall present these
three dimensions and no more.   A fourth dimension

is to us unimaginable—I will not say inconceivable—
we can conceive that a world might be with space
in four dimensions, but we cannot imagine it to
ourselves or think what things would be like
in it.

With difficulty we can perhaps imagine a world
with space of only two dimensions, a "flat land,"
where flat beings of different shapes, like figures cut
out of paper, slide or float about on a flat table.
They could not hop over one another, for they would
only have length and breadth; to hop up you would
want to be able to move in a third dimension, but
having two dimensions only you could only slide
forward and sideways in a plane. To such beings
a ring would be a box. You would have to break
the ring to get anything out of it, for if you tried to
slide out you would be met by a wall in every
direction. You could not jump out of it like a sheep
would jump out of a pen over the hurdles, for to
jump would require a third dimension, which you
have not got. Beings in a world with one dimension only would be in a worse plight still. Like
beads on a string they could slide about in one
direction as far as the others would let them.
They could not pass one another. To such a being
two other beings would be a box one on each side
of him, for if thus imprisoned, he could not get
away. Like a waggon on a railway, he could not
walk round another waggon. That would want

power of moving in two dimensions, still less could he jump over them, that would want three.

We have not the smallest idea why our world has been thus limited. Some philosophers think that the limitation is in us, not in the world, and that perhaps when our minds are free from the limitations imposed by their sojourn in our bodies, and death has set us free, we may see not only what is the length and breadth and height, but a great deal more also of which we can now form no conception. But these speculations lead us out of science into the shadowy land of metaphysics, of which we long to know something, but are condemned to know so little. Area is got by multiplying length by breadth. Cubic content is got by multiplying length by breadth and by height. Of all the conceptions respecting space, that of a line is the simplest. It has direction, and length.

The idea of mass is more difficult to grasp than that of space. It means quantity of matter. But what is matter? That we do not know. It is not weight, though it is true that all matter has weight. Yet matter would still have mass even if its property of weight were taken away.

For consider such a thing as a pound packet of tea. It has size, it occupies space, it has length, breadth, and thickness. It has also weight. But what gives it weight? The attraction of the earth.

Suppose you double the size of the earth. The earth being bigger would attract the package of tea more strongly. The weight of the tea, that is, the attraction of the earth on the package of tea, would be increased—the tea would weigh more than before. Take the package of tea to the planet Jupiter, which, being very large, has an attraction at the surface $2\frac{1}{2}$ times that of the earth. Its size would be the same, but it would feel to carry like a package of sand. Yet there would be the same "mass" of tea. You could make no more cups of tea out of it in Jupiter than on earth. Take it to the moon, and it would weigh a little over two ounces, but still it would be a pound of tea. We are in the habit of estimating mass by its weight, and we do so rightly, for at any place on the earth, as London, the weights of masses are always proportioned to the masses, and if you want to find out what mass of tea you have got, you weigh it, and you know for certain. Hence in our minds we confuse mass with weight. And even in our Acts of Parliament we have done the same thing, so that it is difficult in the statutes respecting standard weights to know what was meant by those who drew them up, and whether a pound of tea means the *mass* of a certain amount of tea or the *weight* of that mass. For accurate thinking we must, of course, always deal with masses, not with weights. For so far as we can tell *mass* appears indestructible. A mass is a mass wherever it is, and for all time, whereas its weight varies with the attractive force of the planet upon which it happens to be, and with its distance from that planet's centre. A flea on this earth can skip perhaps eight inches high; put that flea on the moon, and with the expenditure of the same energy he could skip four feet high. Put him on the planet Jupiter and he could only skip $3\frac{1}{5}$ inches high. A man in a street in the moon could jump up into a window on the first floor of a house. One pound of tea taken to the sun would be as heavy as twenty-eight pounds of it at the earth's surface; and weight varies at different parts of the earth. Hence the true measure of quantity of matter is mass, not weight.

The mass of bodies varies according to their size; if you have the same nature of material, then for a double size you have a double mass. Some bodies are more concentrated than others, that is to say, more dense; it is as though they were more tightly squeezed together. Thus a ball of lead of an inch in diameter contains forty-eight times as much mass as a ball of cork an inch in diameter. In order to know the weight of a certain mass of matter, we should have to multiply the mass by a figure representing the attractive force or pull of the earth.

In physics it is usual to employ the letters of the alphabet as a sort of shorthand to represent words.

So that the letter m stands for the mass of a body. So again g stands for the attractive pull of the earth at a given place. w stands for the weight of the body. Hence then, since the weight of a body depends on its mass and also on the attractive pull of the earth, we express this in short language by saying, $w = m \times g$; or w is equal to m multiplied by g; the symbol $=$ being used for equality, and $\times$ the sign of multiplication. In common use $\times$ is usually omitted, and when letters are put together they are intended to be understood as multiplied. So that this is written

$$w = mg.$$

Of course by this equation we do not mean that weight is mass multiplied into the force of gravity, we only mean that the number of units of weight is to be found by multiplying the number of units of mass into the number of units of the earth's force of gravity.

In the same way, if when estimating the number of waggons, w, that would be wanted for an army of men, n, which consumed a number of pounds, p, of provisions a day, we might put

$$w = np.$$

But this would not mean that we were multiplying soldiers into food to produce waggons, but only that we were performing a numerical calculation.

Time is one of the most mysterious of our elementary ideas. It seems to exist or not to exist, according as we are thinking or not thinking. It seems to run or stand still and to go fast or slowly. How it drags through a wearisome lesson; how it flies during a game of cricket; how it seems to stop in sleep. If we measured time by our own thoughts it would be a very uncertain quantity. But other considerations seem to show us that Nature knows no such uncertainty as regards time, that she produces her phenomena in a uniform manner in uniform times, and that time has an existence independent of our thoughts and wills.

The idea of a state of things in which time existed no more was quite familiar to mediæval thinkers, and was regarded by many of them as the condition that would exist after the Day of Judgment. In recent times Kant propounded the theory that time was only a necessary condition of our thoughts, and had no existence apart from thinking beings—in fact, that it was our way of looking at things.

Scientifically, however, we are warranted in treating time as perfectly real and capable of the most exact measurement. For example, if we arrange a stream of sand to run out of an orifice, and observe how much will run out while an egg is being boiled hard, we find as a fact that if the same quantity of sand runs out, the state of the egg is uniform. If we walk for an hour by a watch, we find that we can go half the distance that we

should if we walked two hours. It is the corre-
spondence of these various experiments that gives
us faith in the treatment of time as a thing
existing independently of ourselves, or, at all events,
independent of our transient moods.

The ideas of time acquired by the races of men
that first evolved from a state of barbarism were
no doubt derived from the observation of day and
night, the month and the year.

For, suppose that a shepherd were on the plains

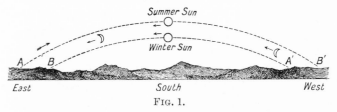

FIG. 1.

of Chaldea, or perhaps on those mountains of India
known as the roof of the world, which according to
some archæologists was the site of the garden of
Eden and the early home of the European race,
what would he see?

He would see the sun rise in the east, slowly
mount the heavens till it stood over the south at
middle day, then it would sink towards the west
and disappear. In summer the rising point of the
sun would be more to the northward than in
winter, and so also would be its point of setting A'.
In winter it would rise a little to the south of east,

and set a little to the south of west, and not rise so high in the heavens at mid-day, so that the summer day would be longer than the winter day. If the day were always divided into twelve hours, whether it were long or short, then in summer the hours of the day would be long; in winter they would be short. This mode of dividing the day was that used by the Greeks. The Egyptians, on the other hand, averaged their day by dividing the whole round of the sun into twenty-four hours, so that the summer day contained more hours than the winter day. Hence, for the Egyptians, sun-rise did not always take place at six clock. For in winter it took place after six, and in summer before six; and this is the system that has descended to us.

The moon also would rise at different places, varying between A and B, and set at places varying between A' and B', but these would be independent of those at which the sun rose and set.

Moreover, the moon each day would appear to get further and further away from the sun in the direction of the arrow, as shown in the sketch. If the moon rose an hour after the sun on one day, the next day it would rise more than two hours after the sun, and so on. This delay in rising of the moon would go on day by day till at last she came right round to the sun again, as shown at M'. And in her path she would change her form from a crescent, as at *M*, up to a full moon, when she would be half way round from the sun, that is, when she would rise twelve hours after him, or just be rising as the sun set. This delay and accompanying change of form would go on, till after three weeks she would have got round to a position *A'*, when she would rise eighteen hours after the sun, and have become a crescent with her back to the sun; in fact, she would always turn her convex side to the sun. At length, when twenty-eight days had passed, she would be round again about opposite to the sun, and consequently her pale light would be extinguished in his beams, and she would gradually reappear as a new moon on the other side of him. This series of changes of the moon takes place once every twenty-eight days, and is called a lunar or "moon" month, and was used as a division of time by very early nations. The changes of the seasons recurred with the changes in the times of rising of the sun, and took a year to bring about. And there were nearly thirteen moon changes in the year.

It was also observed that during its cycle of changes, the sun was slowly moving round backwards among the stars in the same direction as the moon, only it made its retrograde cycle in a year, and thus arose the division of time into months and years. The stars turned round in the heavens once in the complete day. The sun, therefore, appeared to move back among them, passing successively through groups of stars, so as to make the circuit of them all in a year. The stars through which he passed in a year, and through which the moon travelled in a month, were divided by the ancients into groups called constellations, and its yearly path in the heavens was called the zodiac. There were twelve of these constellations in the zodiac called the signs. Hence, then, the sun passed through a sign in every month, making the tour of them all in the year. To these signs fanciful names were given, such as "the Ram," "the Water-bearer," "the Virgin," "the Scorpion," and so on, and the sun and moon were then said to pass through the signs of the zodiac.

Hence, since the path of the sun marked the year, you could tell the seasons by knowing what sign of the zodiac the sun was in. The age of the moon was easily known by her form.

When the winter was over, then, just as the sun set the dog star would be rising in the east, and this would show that the spring was at hand. Then the peasants prepared to till the earth and sow the seed and lead the oxen out to pasture, and celebrated with joyful mirth the glad advent of the spring, corresponding to our Easter, when the sun had run through three constellations of the zodiac. Then came the summer heat, and with many a mystic rite they celebrated Midsummer's Day. In autumn, after three more signs of the zodiac have been traversed by the sun, the sun again rises exactly in the east and sets in the west, and the days and nights are equal. This is the autumnal equinox, and was once celebrated by the feast which we now know as Michaelmas Day, and the goose is the remnant of the ancient festival.

And the great winter feast of the ancients is now known to us as Christmas, and chosen to celebrate the birth of our Lord; for when Christianity came

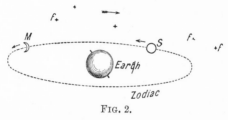

FIG. 2.

into the world and the heathens were converted, the old feast days were deliberately changed into Christian festivals.

To us, therefore, the whole heavens, and the fixed stars with them, appear to turn from east to west, or from left to right, as we look towards the south, as shown by the big arrow. But the moon and sun, though apparently placed in the heavens, move backwards among the fixed stars, as shown by the small arrows. The sun moves at such a rate that he goes round the circle of the heavens in a year of three hundred and sixty-five days. The moon goes round the circle in twenty-eight and a half days, or a lunar month. Of course, in reality the sun is at rest, and it is the earth that moves round the sun and spins on its axis as it moves. But it will presently be shown that the appearance to a person on the earth is the same whether the earth goes round the sun or the sun round the earth.

From the works of Greek writers we know a good deal about the ideas of the world that were entertained by the ancients. The most early notions were, of course, connected with the worship of the gods. The sun was considered as a huge light carried in a chariot, driven by Apollo, with four spirited steeds. It descended to the ocean when the day declined, and then the horses were unyoked by the nymphs of the ocean and led round to the east, so as to be ready for the journey of the following day. The Egyptians figured the sun as placed in a boat which sailed over the heavens. At night the sun god descended into the infernal regions, carrying with him the souls of those who had died during the day. There they passed through different regions of hell, with portals guarded by hideous monsters. Those who had well learned the ritual of the dead knew the words of power wherewith to appease the demons. Those unprovided with the watchwords were subjected to terrible dangers. Then the soul appeared before Minos, and was weighed and dealt with according to its deserts.

The earth was considered as a huge island in the
midst of a circular sea.   Gradually, however, astronomical ideas became subjected to science.   One of
the first truths that dawned on astronomers was
the fact that the earth was a sphere.   For they
noticed that as people went further and further to
the north, the elevation of the sun at midday
above the horizon became smaller and smaller.

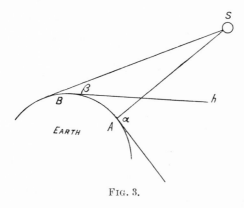

FIG. 3.

This can easily be seen from the diagram.   When
an observer is at *A* the sun appears at an altitude
above the horizon equal to the angle *a*, but as
he goes along the curved surface of the earth to a
point *B* nearer to the north pole, the sun appears
to be lower and only to have an altitude *β*.   From
this it was easy for men so skilled in geometry as
the Greeks to calculate how big the earth was.
They did so, and it appeared to have the enormous

diameter of 8,000 miles. They only knew quite a small portion of it. They thought that the rest was ocean. But they had, of course, a clear idea of the " antipodes " or up-side-down side of it, and they believed that if men were on the other side of it that their feet must all point towards its centre. From this they got the idea of the centre of the earth as a point of attraction for all things that had an earth-seeking or earthy nature. Fire appeared always to desire to go upwards, so they thought that fire had an earth-repellent, heaven-seeking character. Water they thought partly earth-seeking, partly heaven-seeking, for it appeared in the ocean or floated as clouds. Air they thought to be indifferent. And out of the four elements fire, water, earth, and air they believed the world was made. The earth they thought must be at rest ; for if it was in motion things would fly off from it. They saw that either the sun must be moving round the earth, or else the earth must be turning on its axis. They chose the former hypo-thesis, because they argued that if the earth were twisting round once in twenty-four hours then such a country as Greece must be flying round like a spot on the surface of a top, at the rate of about 18,000 miles in twenty-four hours, that is, at the rate of about 180 yards in a second, or faster than an arrow from a bow. But if that was the case then a bird that flew up from the earth would be left far behind. If a ball were thrown up it would fall hundreds of yards behind the person who threw it. They could not conceive how it was possible for a ball thrown up by someone standing on a moving object not to fall behind the thrower.

This decided them in their error. The mistaken astronomy of the Greeks was also much forwarded by Aristotle, the tutor of Alexander the Great. This great genius in politics and philosophy was only in the second rank as a man of science, and, as I think, hardly equal to Archimedes or Hipparchus, or even to Ptolemy. Aristotle wrote a book concerning the heavens which bristles with the most wantonly erroneous scientific ideas, such as, for instance, that the motion of the heavenly bodies must be circular because the most perfect curve is a circle, and similar assumptions as to the course of nature.

The earth, then, being fixed, they thought that the moon, the sun, and the seven planets were carried round it, fixed each of them in an enormous crystal spherical shell. These spheres, like coats of an onion, slid round one upon another, each carrying his celestial luminary. The moon was the nearest, then Mercury, then Venus, then the sun, then Mars, Jupiter and Saturn. Outside them was the sphere of the stars, and outside all the "*primum mobile*," or great Prime Mover of the universe. When one of the celestial bodies, such as the moon, got in front of another, such as the

sun, there was an eclipse. They soon observed that
the moon derived its light from the sun. As they
knew the size of the earth, by comparison they got
some vague idea of the huge distances that the
heavenly bodies must be from us. In fact, they
measured the distance of the moon with approximate accuracy, making it 240,000 miles, or about
thirty times the earth's diameter.

This, of course, gave them the moon's diameter,
for they were easily able to calculate how big an
object must be, that looks as big as the moon and is
240,000 miles away.

This large size of the moon gave them some idea of
the distance of the sun, but they failed to realise
how big and far away he really is.

Several ancient nations used weeks as means of
measuring time. They made four weeks to the
lunar month. The order of the days was rather
curiously arranged. For, assuming that the earth
is the centre of the planetary system, put the
planets in a column, putting the nearest (the moon)
at the bottom and the furthest off at the top—

Saturn,
Jupiter,
Mars,
The Sun,
Venus,
Mercury,
The Moon.

Then divide the day into three watches of eight hours each, and let each watch be presided over by one of the planet-gods: begin with Saturn. We then have Saturn as the first god ruling Saturday, and Jupiter and Mars, the two other gods, for that day. The first watch for Sunday will be the sun; Venus and Mercury will preside over the next two watches of that day. The planet that will preside over the first watch of the next day will be the

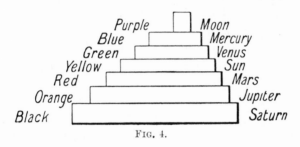

FIG. 4.

moon, and the day will, therefore, be called Monday; Saturn and Jupiter will be the other gods for Monday. The first watch of the next day will be presided over by Mars, and the day will, therefore, be called Mars-day or Mardi, or, in the Teutonic languages, Tuesday, after Tuesco, a Scandinavian god of war. Mercury will give a name to Mercredi, or to Wednesday, or Wodin's-day. Jupiter to Jeudi, or "Thurs" day. Venus to Vendredi, or in the Scandinavian, Friday, the day of the Scandinavian goddess Freya, the goddess of love and beauty, who corresponds to Venus, and thus the week is completed.

This weekly scheme came probably from the Chaldean astronomers. It appears probable that the great tower of Babel, the ruins of which exist to this day, consisted of seven stages, one over the other, the top one painted white, or perhaps purple, to represent the Moon, the next lower blue for Mercury, then green for Venus, yellow for the Sun, red for Mars, orange for Jupiter, and black for Saturn. Unfortunately, of the colours no trace now remains.

But nightly on the long terraces the Babylonian priests observed eclipses and other celestial phenomena. Their records were afterwards taken to Alexandria and kept in the great library that was subsequently burned by the Turks. In that library they were seen by the astronomer Ptolemy, who used them in the writing of his work on astronomy called the "Great Syntaxis" or "Collection." The original work perished, but it had been translated into Arabic by the Arab astronomers, who called it "Al Magest," the Great Book. It was translated from Arabic into Latin, and remained the text-book for astronomers in Europe quite down to the time of Queen Elizabeth, when a better system took its place.

For the use of men engaged in practical astronomy, it is very convenient to consider the sun, moon, stars, and planets as going round the earth at rest. For instance, seamen use the heavenly bodies as in a way hands of a huge clock from which they can know the time and their position on the earth. " The Nautical Almanac," which is printed yearly, gives the true position of these heavenly bodies for every hour, minute, and second of the year, and I will presently show how useful this is to sailors.

We will deal with the sun first. From the motions of the sun we can observe the time. This is done in every garden by means of sun-dials, and I will now describe how they are constructed. If a light, such as the light of a candle, be moved round in a circle at a uniform pace so as to go round once in some given period, such as twenty-four hours, it is obvious that it would serve to measure time. Thus, for example, if a sheet of white paper be placed upon the table, and a pencil be stuck on to it upright with some sealing wax, or a pen propped up in an ink-pot, then a candle held by anyone will cast the shadow of the pen on the paper.

If the person holding the candle walk round the table at a uniform speed, the shadow will go round like the hand of a clock, and might be made to mark the time. If the candle took twenty-four hours to go round the table, as the sun takes twenty-four hours to go round the earth, then marks placed on the paper would serve to measure the hours, and the paper and pen would serve as a sort of sun-dial.

But the sun does not go round the earth as the candle round the table. Its path is an inclined one, like that shown by the dotted line. Sometimes it is above the level of the table, sometimes below

FIG. 5.

it. And, moreover, its winter path is different from its summer path. Whence then it follows that the hour-marks on the paper cannot be put equidistant like the hours on the dial of a clock, and that some arrangement must be made so that the line as shown by the summer sun shall correspond with the time as shown by the winter sun.

Let us suppose that $N\,O\,S$ is the axis of the

heavens, and the lines *N A S*, *N B S*, *N C S*, are
meridian lines drawn from one of the poles *N* of the
heavens round on the surface of a celestial sphere
whose centre is at *O*. Let *A B C* be a circle also

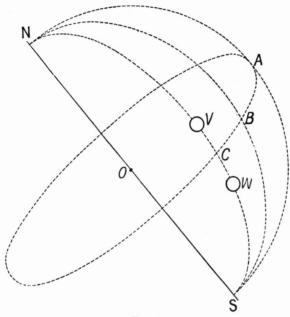

FIG. 6.

on this sphere, passing through *O*, the centre of
the sphere, in a plane at right angles to *N S*, the
axis. Then *A B C* is called the equatorial. It is a
circle in the heavens corresponding to the equator
on the earth. At the vernal and autumnal equinox,

namely on March 25 and September 25, the sun
is in the equatorial.　In midsummer and midwinter it is on opposite sides of the equatorial.
In midsummer it is nearer to N, as at V; in midwinter it is nearer to S, as at W.　Suppose we
were on an island in the midst of a surrounding
ocean, we should only have a limited range of
view.　If the highest point on the island were 100
feet, then from that altitude we should be able to
see about thirteen miles to the horizon.　More
than that could not be seen on account of the
rotundity of the earth.

Let us suppose then such an island surrounded
for thirteen miles distant on every side by an ocean,
and let us consider what would be the apparent
motions of the sun when seen from such an island.
At the vernal and autumnal equinoxes, when the sun
is on the equatorial, it would appear to rise out of
the ocean at a point E, due east; it traverses half the
equatorial and sets in the ocean at a point W, due
west.　The day is twelve hours long, from 6 a.m.
to 6 p.m.

In summer the sun is higher, and nearer to the
pole N, say at a point s.　It rises at a point a in
the ocean more to the north than E, the eastern
point, and sets at a point b, also more north than
W, the western point, and traverses the path $a\ s\ b$.
But to traverse this path it takes longer than
twelve hours, for $a\ s\ b$ is more than half the circle

a s b. Hence then it rises say at 4.30 a.m. and sets
at 7.30 p.m. The night, during which the sun moves
round the path from *b* to *a*, is correspondingly
short, being only nine hours in length, from 7.30

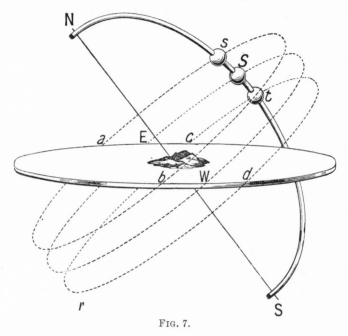

Fig. 7.

p.m. till 4.30 a.m. So you have a long summer
day and a short summer night. But in winter,
when the sun gets nearer to the south pole of
the heavens, it rises at a point *C* in the ocean at
7.30 a.m., and traverses the arc *c t d*, and sets at
the point *d* at 4.30 p.m. So that the winter day is

only nine hours long. But the winter night lasts
from 4.30 p.m. till 7.30 a.m., and is therefore
fifteen hours long, the sun going round the path
d r c in the interval. It is therefore the obliquity
of the poles *N S*, coupled with the fact that the
sun's position is nearer to one pole, *N*, in summer,

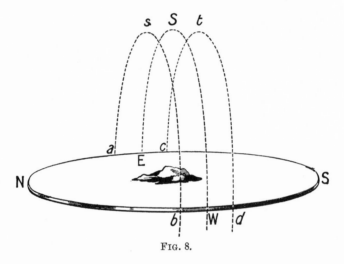

FIG. 8.

and nearer to the other pole, *S*, in winter, that
produces the inequality of days and nights in our
latitudes. Suppose our island were on the equator.
The north pole and the south pole would appear to
be on the horizon, and then whether the sun moved
in the circle *a s b* in the summer, or *E S W* at the
vernal or autumnal equinoxes, or *c t d* in the winter,
in each of these cases, though the places of rising

and setting in the ocean might vary in summer from *a* and *b* to *c* and *d* in winter, yet in each of these cases the path from *a* to *b*, *A* to *B*, and *c* to *d* would still always be a half-circle and occupy twelve hours. Hence at the equator the days and nights never vary in length, but the sun always rises at six and sets at six. And, besides, it always rises straight up from the ocean and plunges down vertically into it, so that there is but little twilight and dawn.

But now let us suppose we were living at the north pole. In this case the north pole would be directly overhead, the south pole directly under our feet. At the vernal and autumnal equinoxes the sun would appear with half its disc above the ocean, and go round the ocean horizon, always appearing with half its disc above the sea. In summer it would appear at a point *s* nearer to the pole *N*. It would go round in the heavens, always appearing above the horizon, and would never set at all. As the summer waned the sun would become lower and lower, still, however, going round and round without setting till at the autumn equinox it reached the horizon. So that for six months it would never have set. But when it did set, there would then be six months without a sun at all.

Thus then all over the world the period of darkness and light is equivalent. At the tropics the

days and nights are always equal. At the poles
light for six months is followed by darkness for six

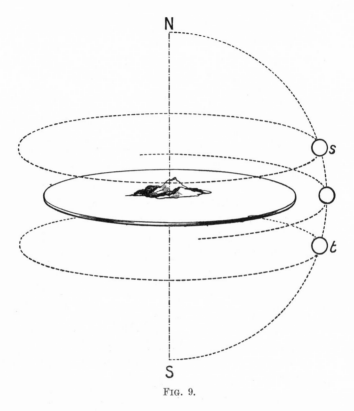

FIG. 9.

months. In the intermediate temperate regions
nights of varying lengths follow days of varying
lengths, a short night following a long day and
vice versâ.

It is evident that for a person living on the
north pole a sun-dial would be an easy thing to
make. All that would be needful would be to put
a post vertically in the ground, and observe its
shadow as the sun
went round (Fig. 10).

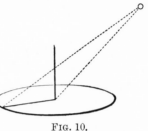

FIG. 10.

In latitudes such as
that of England, where
the pole of the earth
is inclined at an angle
to the horizon, it is
necessary that the rod,
or " style " as it is
called, of the sun-dial should be inclined to the
horizontal. For if we used an upright " style," as
$O A$, then when the sun was in the south, at midday,
the shadow would lie along the same direction,
$O B$, whether the sun
were high in summer,
as at S, or low in
winter, as at s. But
at other hours, such
as nine o'clock in the
morning, the shadow of
the " style " $O A$ would,

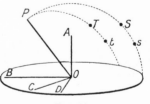

FIG. 11.

when the sun was at its summer position T, lie
along $O D$, whereas when the sun was at its winter
position t the shadow would lie along $O C$. Thus
the time would appear different in summer and in

D 2

winter ; and the dial would lead to errors. But if the " style " is inclined in the direction of the poles, then, however, the sun moves from or towards the pole. As its position varies in winter and summer, the shadow still remains unchanged for any particular hour, and it is only the circular motion of the sun round in its daily path that affects the position of the shadows.

Therefore the first condition of making a sun-dial

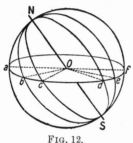

FIG. 12.

is that the " style " which casts the shadow should be parallel to the earth's axis, that is to say should point to the polar star. This is the case whether the sun-dial is horizontal or is vertical, and whether it stands on a pillar in the garden or is attached to the wall of a house.

To divide the dial, we have only to imagine it surrounded by a sort of cage formed of twenty-four arcs drawn from the north pole to the south pole, and equidistant from one another. In its course the sun would cross one of them every hour. Hence the points to which the shadows *o a, o b, o c, o d*, of the inclined " style " *O N* would point are the points where these arcs meet the horizontal circle. This consideration leads to a simple method of constructing a sun-dial, which is given at the end of this chapter in an appendix.

Sun-dials were largely in use in ancient times. It is thought that the circular rows of stones used by the Druids were used to mark the sun's path, and indicate the times and seasons. Obelisks are also supposed to have been used to cast sun-shadows. The Greeks were perfectly ac-quainted with the method of making sun-dials with inclined "styles," or "gnomons."

FIG. 13.

Small portable sun-dials were once much used before the in-troduction of watches, and were provided with compasses by which they could be turned round, so that the "style" pointed to the north.

Sun-dials were only available during the hours of the day when the sun was shining. The desire to mark the hours of the night led to the adoption of water clocks, which measured time by the amount of water which escaped from a small hole in a level of water. Some care, however, is required to secure correct registration. For suppose that we have a vessel with a small pipe leading out near the bottom, then the amount of water which will run out of the pipe in a given time depends upon the pressure

of the water at the pipe, and this depends in its turn
upon $P\,Q$, the head of water in the vessel. Whence
it follows that the division $Q\,R$, due to say an hour's
run of the clock at $Q\,R$, will be more than $q\,r$,
the division corresponding to an hour, at q, a point
lower down between P and Q, and hence the
divisions marked on the vessel to show the hours
by means of the level of the water would be uneven,
becoming smaller and smaller as the water fell in
the vessel.

To avoid the inconvenience of unequal divisions,
the water to be measured was allowed to escape into
an empty vessel from a vessel in which its surface
was always kept at a constant level. Inasmuch as
the pressure on the pipe or orifice in the vessel in
which the water was always kept at a constant
level was always constant, it followed that equal
volumes of water indicated equal times, and the
vessel into which the water fell needed only to be
equally divided.

As a measure of hours of the day in countries
such as Egypt, where the hours were always equal,
and thus where the longer days contained more
hours, the water clock was very suitable; but in
Greece and Rome, where the day, whatever its
length, was always divided into twelve hours, the
simple water clock was as unsuitable as a modern
clock would be, for it always divided the hours
equally, and took no account of the fact that by

such a system the hours in summer were longer than in winter.

In order, therefore, to make the water clock available in Greece and Italy, it became necessary to make the hours unequal, and to arrange them to correspond with unequal hours of the Greek day. This plan was accomplished as follows. Upon the water which was poured into the vessel that measured the hours was placed a float; and on the float stood a figure made of thin copper, with a wand in its hand. This wand pointed to an unequally divided scale. A separate scale was provided for every day in the year, and these scales were mounted on a drum which revolved so as to turn round once in the year. Thus as the figure rose each day by means of a cogwheel it moved the drum round one division, or one three hundred and sixty-fifth part of a revolution. By this means the scale corresponding to any particular day of winter or summer was brought opposite the wand of the figure, and thus the scale of hours was kept true. In fact, the water clock, which kept true time, was made by artificial means to keep untrue time, in order to correspond with the unequal hours of the Greek days. In the picture A is the receiving water vessel, P the pipe through which the water flows; B is the figure, C the rod; D is the drum, made to revolve by the cogwheel E, containing 365 teeth, of which one tooth was driven forward at the close of

each day. A syphon *G* was fixed in the vessel *A*, so
that when the figure had risen to the top and pushed

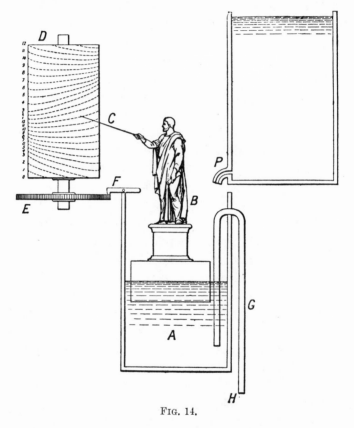

FIG. 14.

forward the lever *F*, the syphon suddenly emptied
the vessel through the pipe *H*, and the figure fell
to the bottom of the vessel *A* and became ready to

rise and register another day. The divisions on the drum are, of course, uneven. On one side, corresponding to the summer, the day hours would reckon about seventy minutes each, the night hours would be only about fifty minutes each, so that the day divisions on the scale would be long, and the night divisions short. The reverse would be the case in winter. And, therefore, the lines round the drum would go in an uneven wavy form.

Such water clocks as these were used by the ancient Romans.

Sand was also used to measure time. As soon as the art of blowing glass had been perfected by the people of Byzantium, from whom the art passed to the Venetians, sand-glasses were made. These glasses were used for all sorts of purposes, for speeches and for cooking, but their most important use was at sea. For it was very important in the early days of navigation to know the speed at which the vessel was proceeding in order that one's place at sea might be calculated. The earliest method was to throw over a heavy piece of wood of a shape that resisted being dragged through the water, and with a string tied to it. The block of wood was called the log, and the string had knots in it. The knots were so arranged that when one of them ran through one's fingers in a half-minute measured by a sand-glass it indicated that the vessel was going at the speed of one nautical mile in

an hour.   The nautical mile was taken so that sixty
of them constituted one degree, that is one three
hundred and sixtieth part of a great circle of the
earth.   Each nautical mile has, therefore, 6,080 feet.
This is bigger than an ordinary mile on land, which
has only 5,280 feet.   The knots, therefore, have to be
arranged so that when the ship is going one nautical
mile—that is to say, 6,080 feet—in an hour, a knot
shall run out during the half-minute run of the
minute glass.   This is attained by putting the knots
$\frac{1}{120} \times 6,080 = 50$ feet 7 inches apart. As one sailor
heaved the log over he gave a stamp on the deck
and allowed the cord to run out through his fingers.
Another sailor then turned the sand-glass.   When
the sand had all run out, showing that half a minute
had passed, the man who was letting the cord run
through his fingers gripped it fast, and observed
how many knots or parts of knots of string had
run out, and thus was able to tell how many
" knots " per half-minute the vessel was going,
that is to say, how many nautical miles an hour.

The modern plan of observing the speed of vessels
is different.   Now we use a patent log, consisting
of a miniature screw propeller tied to a string and
dragged through the water after the vessel.   As it
is pulled through the water it revolves, and the
number of revolutions it makes shows how much
water it has passed through, and thus what distance
it has gone. The number of revolutions is measured

by a counting mechanism, and can be read off when
the log is pulled in. Or sometimes the screw is
attached to a stiff wire, and the counting mechanism
is kept on board the ship.

We use the expression "knots an hour" quite
incorrectly. It should be "knots per half-minute,"
or "nautical miles an hour."

It is easy to use the flow of sand for all sorts of
purposes to measure time. Thus, if sand be allowed
to flow from a hopper through a fine hole into a
bucket, the bucket may be arranged so that when
a given time has elapsed, and a given weight of sand
has therefore fallen, the bucket shall tip over, and
release a catch, which shall then allow a weight to
fall and any mechanical operation to be done that is
required. Thus, for example, we might put an egg
in a small holder tied to a string and lower it into
a saucepan of boiling water. The string might have
a counter-weight attached to it, acting over a pulley
and thus always trying to pull it up out of the
water. But this might be prevented by a pin passing through a loop in the string and preventing it
moving. A hopper or funnel might be filled with
sand which was allowed gradually to escape into a
small tip-waggon or other similar device, so that
when a given amount of sand had entered the tip-
waggon would tip over, lurch the pin out of the
loop, and thus release the weight, which in its turn
would pull the egg up out of the water in three

minutes or any desired time after it had been put
in, or a hole could be made in the saucepan, furnished with a little tap, and the water that ran out
might be made to fall into a tip-waggon and tip it
over, and thus when it had run out to put an
extinguisher on to the spirit lamp that was heating

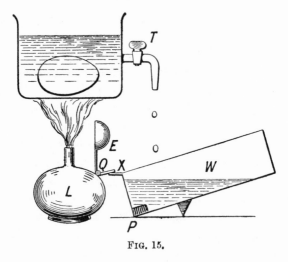

FIG. 15.

the saucepan, and at the same time make a contact
and ring an electric bell. By this means the egg
would be always exactly cooked to the right amount,
would be kept warm after it was cooked, and a signal
given when it was ready.

The sketch shows such an arrangement. The
saucepan is about three inches in diameter and two
inches high. When filled with water it will hold

an egg comfortably. The extinguisher E, mounted on a hinge Q, is turned back, and the spirit lamp L is lit. As soon as the water boils, the tap T is turned, and the water gradually trickles away into the tip-waggon. As soon as it is full it tips over and strikes the arm X of the extinguisher, and turns the lamp out. The little hot water left in the saucepan will keep the egg warm for some time.

The waggon W must have a weight P at one end of it, and the fulcrum must be nearer to that end, so that when empty it rests with the end P down, but when full it tips over on the fulcrum, when the waggon has received the right quantity of water. I leave to the ingenious reader the task of working out the details of such a machine, which, if made properly, will act very well and may be made for a number of eggs and worked with very little trouble.

FIG. 16.

Mercury has been used also as an hour-glass. The orifice must be exceedingly fine. Or a bubble of mercury may be put into a tube which contains air, and made gradually as it falls to drive the air out through a minute hole. The difficulty is to get the hole fine enough. All that can be done is to draw out a fine tube in the blow-lamp, break it off, and put the broken point in the blow-lamp until it is almost completely closed up. A tube may thus be made about twelve inches long that will take

twelve hours for a bubble of mercury to descend in
it. But the trouble of making so small a hole is
considerable.

King Alfred is said to have used candles made of
wax to mark the time. As they blew about with
the draughts, he put them in lanterns of horn.
They had no glass
windows in those days,
but only openings
closed with heavy
wooden shutters. These
large shutters were for
use in fine weather.
Smaller shutters were
made in them, so as to
let a little light in in
rainy weather without
letting in too much
wind and rain.

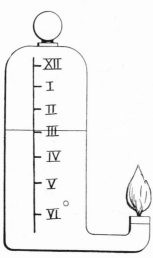

Fig. 17.

Rooms must then
have been very
draughty, so that people
required to wear caps and gowns, and beds had
thick curtains drawn round them. When glass
was first invented it was only used by kings and
princes, and glass casements were carried about with
them to be fixed into the windows of the houses to
which they came, and removed at their departure.

Oil lamps were also used to mark the time.

Some of them certainly as early as the fifteenth century were made like bird-bottles; that is to say, they consisted of a reservoir closed at the top with a pipe leading out of the bottom. When full, the pressure of the external atmosphere keeps the oil in the bottle, and the oil stands in the neck and feeds the wick. As the oil is consumed bubbles of air pass back along the neck and rise up to the top of the oil, the level of which gradually sinks. Of course the time shown by the lamp varies with the rate of burning of the oil, and hence with the size of the wick, so that the method of measuring time is a very rough one.

<h2 style="text-align:center">APPENDIX.</h2>

To make a sun-dial, procure a circular piece of zinc, about ⅛ inch thick, and say twelve inches in diameter. Have a "style" or "gnomon" cast such that the angle of its edge equals the latitude of the place where the sun-dial is to be set up. This for London will be equal to 51° 30″. A pattern may be made for this in wood; it should then be cast in gun-metal, which is much better for out-of-door exposure than brass. On a sheet of paper draw a circle $A\ B\ C$ with centre O. Make the angle $B\ O\ D$ equal to the latitude of the place for London $= 51°\ 30″$. From A draw $A\ E$ parallel to $O\ B$ to meet $O\ D$ in E, and with radius $O\ E$ describe another circle about O. Divide the inner circle A B C into twenty-four parts, and draw radii through them from O to meet the larger circle. Through any divisions (say that corresponding to two o'clock) draw lines parallel to O B, O C, respectively to meet in a. Then the line O a is the shadow line of the gnomon at two o'clock. The lines thus drawn on paper may be transferred

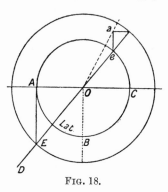

FIG. 18.

to the dial and engraved on it, or else eaten in with acid in the manner in which etchings are done.

The centre O need not be in the centre of the zinc disc, but may be on one side of it, so as to give better room for the hours, etc. A motto may be etched upon the dial, such as "Horas non numero nisi serenas," or "Qual 'hom senza Dio, son senza sol io," or any suitable inscription, and the dial is ready for use. It is best put up by turning it till the hour is shown truly as compared with a correctly timed watch. It must be levelled with a spirit level. It must be remembered that the sun does not move quite uniformly in his yearly path among the fixed stars. This is because he

moves not in a circle, but in an ellipse of which
the earth is in one of the foci. Hence the hours
shown on the dial are slightly irregular, the sun
being sometimes in advance of the clock, sometimes
behind it. The difference is never more than a

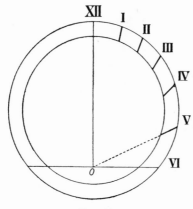

FIG. 19.

quarter of an hour. There is no difference at
midsummer and midwinter.

Civil time is solar time averaged, so as to make the
hours and days all equal. The difference between
civil time and apparent solar time is called the
equation of time, and is the amount by which the
sun-dial is in advance of or in retard of the clock.
In setting a dial by means of a watch, of course
allowance must be made for the equation of time.

CHAPTER II.

In the last chapter a short description has been given of the ideas of the ancients as to the nature of the earth and heavens. Before we pass to the changes introduced by modern science, it will be well to devote a short space to an examination of ancient scientific ideas.

All science is really based upon a combination of two methods, called respectively inductive and deductive reasoning. The first of these consists in gathering together the results of observation and experiment, and, having put them all together, in the formulation of universal laws. Having, for example, long observed that all heavy things tended to go towards the centre of the earth, we might conclude that, since the stars remain up in the sky, they can have no weight. The conclusion would be wrong in this case, not because the method is wrong, but because it is wrongly applied. It is true that all heavy things *tend* to go to the centre of the earth, but if they are being whirled round like a stone in a sling the centrifugal force will counteract this tendency. The first part of the reasoning would be inductive, the econd deductive. All this reasoning consists, therefore, in forming as complete an idea as possible respecting the nature of a thing, and then concluding from that idea what the thing will do or what its other properties will be. In fact, you form correct ideas, or " concepts," as they are called, and reason from them.

But the danger arises when you begin to reason before you are sure of the nature of your concepts, and this has been the great source of error, and it was this error that all men of science so commonly fell into all through ancient and modern times up to the seventeenth century.

Of course, if it were possible by mere observation to derive a complete knowledge of any objects, it would be the simplest method. All that would be necessary to do would be to reason correctly from this knowledge. Unfortunately, however, it is not possible to obtain knowledge of this kind in any branch of science.

The ancient method resembled the action of one who should contend that by observing and talking to a man you could acquire such a knowledge of his character as would infallibly enable you to understand and predict all his actions, and to take little trouble to see whether what he did verified your predictions.

The only difference between the old methods and the new is that in modern times men have learned to give far more care to the formation of correct ideas to start with, are much more cautious in arguing from them, and keep testing them again and again on every possible opportunity.

The constant insistence on the formation of clear ideas and the practice of, as Lord Bacon called it, "putting nature to the torture," is the main cause of the advance of physical science in modern times, and the want of application of these principles explains why so little progress is being made in the so-called "humanitarian" studies, such as philosophy, ethics, and politics.

The works of Aristotle are full of the fallacious method of the old system. In his work on the heavens he repeatedly argues that the heavenly bodies must move in circles, because the circle is the most perfect figure. He affects a perplexity as to how a circle can at the same time be convex and also its opposite, concave, and repeatedly entangles his readers in similar mere word confusion.

Regarded as a man of science, he must be placed, I think, in spite of his great genius, below Archimedes, Hipparchus, and several other ancient astronomers and physicists.

His errors lived after him and dominated the thought of the middle ages, and for a long time delayed the progress of science.

The other great writer on astronomy of ancient times was Ptolemy of Alexandria.

His work was called the "Great Collection," and was what we should now term a compendium of astronomy. Although based on a fundamental error, it is a thoroughly scientific work. There is none of the false philosophy in it that so much disfigures the work of Aristotle. The reasons for believing that the earth is at rest are interesting. Ptolemy argues that if the earth were moving round on its axis once in twenty-four hours a bird that flew up from it would be left behind. At first sight this argument seems very convincing, for it appears impossible to conceive a body spinning at the rate at which the earth is alleged to move, and yet not leaving behind any bodies that become detached from it.

On the other hand, the system which taught that the sun and planets moved round the earth, and which had been adopted largely on account of its supposed simplicity, proved, on further examination, to be exceedingly complicated. Each planet, instead of moving simply and uniformly round the earth in a circle, had to be supposed to move uniformly in a circle round another point that moved round the earth in a circle. This secondary circle, in which the planet moved, was called an epicycle. And even this more complicated view failed to explain the facts.

A system which, like that of Aristotle and Ptolemy, was based on deductions from concepts,

and which consisted rather of drawing conclusions
than of examining premises, was very well adapted
to mediæval thought, and formed the foundation
of astronomy and geography as taught by the
schoolmen.

The poem of Dante accurately represents the
best scientific knowledge of his day. According
to his views, the centre of the earth was a fixed

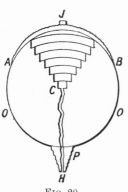

FIG. 20.

point, such that all things
of a heavy nature tended
towards it. Thus the earth
and water collected round
it in the form of a ball.
He had no idea of the
attraction of one particle
of matter for another particle. The only concep-
tion he had of gravity
was of a force drawing all
heavy things to a certain
point, which thus became the point round which the
world was formed. The habitable part of the earth
was an island, with Jerusalem in the middle of
it J. Round this island was an ocean O. Under
the island, in the form of a hollow cone, was
hell, with its seven circles of torment, each circle
becoming smaller and smaller, till it got down
into the centre C. Heaven was at the opposite
side H of the earth to Jerusalem, and was

beyond the circles of the planets, in the *primum mobile*. When Lucifer was expelled from heaven after his rebellion against God, having become of a nature to be attracted to the centre of the earth, and no longer drawn heavenwards, he fell from heaven, and impinged upon the earth just at the antipodes of Jerusalem, with such violence that he plunged right through it to the centre, throwing up behind him a hill. On the summit of this hill was the Garden of Eden, where our first parents lived, and down the sides of the hill was a spiral winding way which constituted purgatory. Dante, having descended into hell, and passed the centre, found his head immediately turned round so as to point the other way up, and, having ascended a tortuous path, came out upon the hill of Purgatory. Having seen this, he was conducted to the various spheres of the planets, and in each sphere he became put into spiritual communion with the spirits of the blessed who were of the character represented by that sphere, and he supposes that he was thus allowed to proceed from sphere to sphere until he was permitted to come into the presence of the Almighty, who in the *primum mobile* presided over the celestial hosts.

The astronomical descriptions given by Dante of the rising and setting of the sun and moon and planets are quite accurate, according to the system of the world as conceived by him, and show not only that he was a competent astronomer, but that he probably possessed an astrolabe and some tables of the motions of the heavenly bodies.

Our own poet Chaucer may also be credited with accurate knowledge of the astronomy of his day. His poems often mention the constellations, and one of them is devoted to a description of the astrolabe, an instrument somewhat like the celestial globe which used to be employed in schools.

But with the revival of learning in Europe and the rise of freedom of thought, the old theories were questioned in more than one quarter.

It occurred to Copernicus, an ecclesiastic who lived in the sixteenth century, to re-examine the theory that had been started in ancient times, and to consider what explanation of the appearance of the heavenly bodies could be given on the hypothesis put forward by Pythagoras, that the earth moved round on its own axis, and also round the sun.

It may appear rather curious that two theories so different, one that the sun goes round the earth and the other that the earth goes round the sun, should each be capable of explaining the observed appearances of those bodies. But it must be remembered that motion is relative. If in a waltz the gentleman goes round the lady, the lady also goes round the gentleman. If you take away the room in which they are turning, and consider them as spinning round like two insects in space, who is to say which of them is at rest and which in motion? For motion is relative. I can consider motion in a train from London to York. As I leave London I get nearer to York, and I move with respect to London and York. But if both London and York were annihilated how should I know that I was in motion at all? Or, again, if, while I was at rest in the train at a station on the way, instead of the train moving the whole earth began to move in a southward direction, and the train in some way were left stationary, then, though the earth was moving, and the train was at rest, yet, so far as I was concerned, the train would appear to have started again on its journey to York, at which place it would appear to arrive in due time. The trees and hedges would fly by at the proper rate, and who was to say whether the train was in motion or the earth?

The theory of Copernicus, however, remained but a theory. It was opposed to the evidence of the senses, which certainly leads us to think that the earth is at rest, and it was opposed also to the ideas of some among the theologians who thought that the Bible taught us that the earth was so fast that it could not be moved. Therefore the

theory found but little favour. It was in fact
necessary before the question could be properly
considered on its merits that more should be
known about the laws of motion, and this was
the principal work of Galileo.

The merit of Galileo is not only to have placed
on a firm basis the study of mechanics, but to
have set himself definitely and consciously to
reverse the ancient methods of learning.

He discarded authority, basing all knowledge
upon reason, and protested against the theory
that the study of words could be any substitute
for the study of things.

Alluding to the mathematicians of his day, " This
sort of men," says Galileo in a letter to the
astronomer Kepler, " fancied that philosophy was
to be studied like the ' Æneid ' or ' Odyssey,' and
that the true reading of nature was to be detected
by the collating of texts." And most of his life was
spent in fighting against preconceived ideas. It
was maintained that there could only be seven
planets, because God had ordered all things in
nature by sevens ("Dianoia Astronomica," 1610) ;
and even the discoveries of the spots on the sun
and the mountains in the moon were discredited
on the ground that celestial bodies could have no
blemishes. " How great and common an error,"
writes Galileo, " appears to me the mistake of those
who persist in making their knowledge and

apprehension the measure of the knowledge and
apprehension of God, as if that alone were perfect which they understand to be so. But . . . .
nature has other scales of perfection, which
we, being unable to comprehend, class among
imperfections.

"If one of our most celebrated architects had
had to distribute the vast multitude of fixed
stars over the great vault of heaven, I believe he
would have disposed them with beautiful arrangements of squares, hexagons, and octagons; he
would have dispersed the larger ones among the
middle-sized or lesser, so as to correspond exactly
with each other; and then he would think he had
contrived admirable proportions; but God, on the
contrary, has shaken them out from His hand as
if by chance, and we, forsooth, must think that
He has scattered them up yonder without any
regularity, symmetry, or elegance."

In one of Galileo's "Dialogues" Simplicio says,
"That the cause that the parts of the earth move
downwards is notorious, and everyone knows that
it is gravity." Salviati replies, "You are out, Master
Simplicio: you should say that everyone knows
that *it is called* gravity; I do not ask you for the
name, but for the nature, of the thing of which
nature neither you nor I know anything."

Too often are we still inclined to put the name
for the thing, and to think when we use big words

such as art, empire, liberty, and the rights of
man, that we explain matters instead of obscuring
them.   Not one man in a thousand who uses them
knows what he means; no two men agree as to
their signification.

The relativity of motion mentioned above was
very elegantly illustrated by Galileo.   He called
attention to the fact that if an artist were making
a drawing with a pen while in a ship that was in
rapid passage through the water, the true line
drawn by the pen with regard to the surface of the
earth would be a long straight line with some small
dents or variations in it.   Yet the very same line
traced by the pen upon a paper carried along in the
ship made up a drawing.   Whether you saw a long
uneven line or a drawing in the path that the pen
had traced depended altogether on the point of
view with which you regarded its motion.

But the first great step in science which Galileo
made when quite a young professor at Pisa was the
refutation of Aristotle's opinion that heavy bodies
fell to the earth faster than light ones.   In the
presence of a number of professors he dropped
two balls, a large and a small one, from the
parapet of the leaning tower of Pisa.   They fell to
the ground almost exactly in the same time.   This
experiment is quite an easy one to try.   One of the
simplest ways is as follows: Into any beam (the
lintel of a door will do), and about four inches apart,

drive three smooth pins so as to project each about a
quarter of an inch; they must not have any heads.

Fig. 21.

Take two unequal weights, say of 1 lb. and 3 lbs.
Anything will do, say a boot for one and pocket-
knife for the other; fasten loops of fine string to

them, put the loops over the centre peg of the
three, and pass the strings one over each of the
side pegs.   Now of course if you hitch the loops off
the centre peg P the objects will be released together.
This can be done by making a loop at the end of
another piece of string, A, and putting it on to the
centre peg behind the other loops.   If the string
be pulled of course the loop on it pulls the other
two loops off the central peg, and allows the boot
and the knife to drop.
The boot and the knife
should be hung so as to
be at the same height.
They will then fall to the
ground together.   The
same experiment can be
tried by dropping two
objects from an upper
window, holding one in
each hand, and taking care to let them go together.

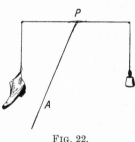

FIG. 22.

This result is very puzzling ; one does not understand it.   It appears as though two unequal forces
produced the same effect.   It is as though a strong
horse could run no faster than a weaker one.

The professors were so irritated at the result of
this experiment, and indeed at the general character
of young Professor Galileo's attacks on the time-
honoured ideas of Aristotle, that they never rested
till they worried him out of his very poorly paid

chair at Pisa. He then took a professorship at Padua.

Let us now examine this result and see why it is that the ideas we should at first naturally form are wrong, and that the heavy body will fall in exactly the same time as the light one.

We may reason the matter in this way. The heavy body has more force pulling on it; that is true, but then, on the other hand there is more matter which has got to be moved. If a crowd of persons are rushing out of a building, the total force of the crowd will be greater than the force of one man, but the speed at which they can get out will not be greater than the speed of one man; in fact, each man in the crowd has only force enough to move his own mass. And so it is with the weights: each part of the body is occupied in moving itself. If you add more to the body you only add another part which has itself to move. A hundred men by taking hands cannot run faster than one man.

But, you will say, cannot a man run faster than a child? Yes, because his impelling power is greater in proportion to his weight than that of a child.

If it were the fact that the attraction of gravity due to the earth acted on some bodies with forces greater in proportion to their masses than the forces that acted on other bodies, then it is true

that those different bodies would fall in unequal
time. But it is an experimental fact that the
attractive force of gravity is always exactly proportional to the mass of a body, and the resistance to
motion is also proportional to mass, hence the force
with which a body is moved by the earth's attraction
is always proportional to the difficulty of moving
the body. This would not be the case with other
methods of setting a body in motion. If I kick a
small ball with all my might, I shall send it further
than a kick of equal strength would send a heavier
ball. Why? Because the impulse is the same in
each case, but the masses are different. But if
those balls are pulled by gravity, then, by the very
nature of the earth's attraction (the reason of which
we cannot explain), the small ball receives a little
pull, and the big ball receives a big pull, the earth
exactly apportioning its pull in each case to the
mass of the body on which it has to act. It is to
this fact, that the earth pulls bodies with a strength
always in each case exactly proportional to their
masses, that is due the result that they fall in
equal times, each body having a pull given to it
proportional to its needs.

The error of the view of Aristotle was not only
demonstrated by Galileo by experiment, but was
also demonstrated by argument. In this argument
Galileo imitated the abstract methods of the
Aristotelians, and turned those methods against

themselves. For he said, "You" (the Aristotelians) "say that a lighter body will fall more slowly than a heavy one. Well, then, if you bind a light body on to a heavy one by means of a string, and let them fall together, the light body ought to hang behind, and impede the heavy body, and thus the two bodies together ought to fall more slowly than the heavy body alone; this follows from your view: but see the contradiction. For the two bodies tied together constitute a heavier body than the heavy body alone, and thus, on your own theory, ought to fall more quickly than the heavy body alone. Your theory, therefore, contradicts itself."

The truth is that each body is occupied in moving itself without troubling about moving its neighbour, so that if you put any number of marbles into a bag and let them drop they all go down individually, as it were, and all in the time which a single marble would take to fall. For any other result would be a contradiction. If you cut a piece of bread in two, and put the two halves together, and tie them together with a thread, will the mere fact that they are two pieces make each of them fall more slowly than if they were one? Yet that is what you would be bound to assert on the Aristotelian theory. Hold an egg in your open hand and jump down from a chair. The egg is not left behind; it falls with you. Yet you are the heavier of the two, and on Aristotelian principles you ought to leave the egg behind you. It is true that when you jump down a bank your straw hat will often come off, but that is because the air offers more resistance to it than the air offers to your body. It is the downward rush through the air that causes your hat to be left behind, just as wind will blow your hat off without blowing you away. For since motion is relative, it is all one whether you jump down through the air, or the air rushes past you, as in a wind. If there were no air, the hat would fall as fast as your body.

This is easy to see if we have an airpump and are thus enabled to pump out almost all the air from a glass vessel. In that vessel so exhausted, a feather and a coin will fall in equal times. If we have not an airpump, we can try the experiment in a more simple way. For let us put a feather into a metal egg-cup and drop them together. The cup will keep the air from the feather, and the feather will not come out of the cup. Both will fall to the ground together. But if the lighter body fall more slowly, the feather ought to be left behind. If, however, you tie some strings across a napkin ring so as to make a sort of rough sieve, and put a feather in it, and then drop the ring, then as the ring falls the air can get through the bottom of the ring and act on the feather, which will be left floating as the ring falls.

Let us now go on to examine the second fallacy

that was derived from the Aristotelians, and that so long impeded the advance of science, namely, that the earth must be at rest.

The principal reason given for this was that if bodies were thrown up from the earth they ought, if the earth were in motion, to remain behind. Now, if this were so, then it would follow that if a person in a train which was moving rapidly threw a ball vertically, that is perpendicularly, up into the air, the ball, instead of coming back into his hand, ought to hit the side of the carriage behind him. The next time any of my readers travel by train he can easily satisfy himself that this is not so. But there are other ways of proving it. For instance, if a little waggon running on rails has a spring gun fixed in it in a perpendicular position, so arranged that when the waggon comes to a particular point on the rails a catch releases the trigger and shoots a ball perpendicularly upwards, it will be found that the ball, instead of going upwards in a vertical line, is carried along over the waggon, and the ball as it ascends and descends keeps always above the waggon, just as a hawk might hover over a running mouse, and finally falls not behind the waggon, but into it.

So, again, if an article is dropped out of the window of a train, it will not simply be left behind as it falls, but while it falls it will also partake of the motion of the train, and touch the ground, not behind the point from which it was dropped, but just underneath it.

The reason is, that when the ball is dropped or thrown it acquires not only the motion given to it by the throw, or by gravity, but it takes also the motion of the train from which it is thrown. If a ball is thrown from the hand, it derives its motion from the motion of the hand, and if at the time of throwing the person who does so is moving rapidly along in a train, his hand has not only the outward motion of the throw, but also the onward motion of the train, and the ball therefore acquires both motions simultaneously. Hence then it is not correct reasoning to say, because a ball thrown up vertically falls vertically back to the spot from which it was thrown, that therefore the earth must be at rest; the same result will happen whether the earth is at rest or in motion. You can no more tell whether the earth is at rest or in motion from the behaviour of falling bodies than you can tell whether a ship on the ocean is at rest or in motion from the behaviour of bodies on it.

But you will say. Then why do we feel sea-sick on a ship? The answer is, that that is because the motion of the ship is not uniform. If the earth, instead of turning round uniformly, were to rock to and fro, everything on it would be flung about in the wildest fashion. For as soon as the earth had communicated its motion to a body which then moved with the earth, if the earth's motion were reversed, the body would go on like a passenger in a train on which the break is quickly applied, and he would be shot up against the side of the room. Nay, more, the houses would be shaken off their foundations. Changes of motion are perceptible *so long as the change is going on.* We are therefore justified in inferring from the behaviour of bodies on the earth, not that the earth is at rest, but that it is either at rest, or else, if it is in motion, that its motion is uniform and not in jerks or variable.

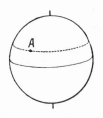

FIG. 23.

For if it were not so, consider what would be happening around us. The earth is about 8,000 miles in diameter, and a parallel of latitude through London is therefore about 19,000 miles long, and this space is travelled in twenty-four hours. So that London is spinning through space at the rate of over 1,000 feet a second, due to the earth's rotary motion alone, not to speak of the motion due to the earth's path round the sun. If a boy jumped up two and a half feet into the air, he would take about half a second to go up and come down, but if in jumping he did not partake of the earth's motion, he would land more than 500 feet to the westward of the point from which he jumped up, and if he did it in a room, he would be dashed against the wall with a force greater than he would experience from a drop down from the top of Mont Blanc. He would be not only killed, but dashed into an indistinguishable mass. If the earth suddenly stood still, everything on it would be shaken to pieces. It is bad enough to have the concussion of a train going thirty miles an hour when dashed against some obstacle. But the concussion due to the earth's stoppage would be as of a train going about 800 miles an hour, which would smash up everything and everybody.

Thus, then, the first effect of the new ideas formulated by Galileo was to show that the Copernican theory that the earth moved round on its axis, and round the sun, was in agreement with the laws of motion. In fact, he introduced quite new ideas of force, and these ideas I must now endeavour to explain.

Let us consider what is meant by the word "force." If I press my hand against the table, I exert force. The harder I press, the more force there is. If I put a weight on a stand, the weight presses the stand down with a force. If I squeeze a spring, the spring tries to recover itself and exerts a certain force. In all these cases force is considered as a pressure. And I can measure the force by seeing how much it will press things. If I take a spring, and press it in an inch, it takes perhaps a force of

1 lb. It will take a force of 2 lbs. to press it in another inch. Or again, if I pull it out an inch, it takes a force of 1 lb. If I pull it out another inch, it takes a force of 2 lbs. We thus always get into the habit of conceiving forces as producing pressures and being measured by pressures.

This is a perfectly legitimate way of looking at the matter, just as the cook's method of employing a spring balance to weigh masses of meat is a perfectly legitimate way of estimating the forces acting upon bodies at rest. But when you come to consider the laws of the pendulums of clocks, to which all that I am saying is a preparation, then you have to deal with bodies in motion. And for this purpose a new idea of force altogether is requisite.

FIG. 24.

We shall no longer speak of forces as producing *pressures*. We shall treat them quite independently of their pressing power. The sun exerts a force of attraction on the earth, but it does not press upon it. It exerts its force at a distance. Hence then we want a new idea of "force." This idea is to be the following. We will consider that when a force acts upon a body it endeavours to cause it to move; in fact, it tries to impart motion to the body. We may treat this motion as a sort of thing or property. The longer the force acts on the body, the more motion it imparts to it, provided the body is free to receive that motion. So that we may say that the test of the strength of the force is how much motion it can give to a body of a given mass in a given time. It does not matter how the force acts. It may act by means of a string and pull it; it may act by means of a stick and push it; it may act by attraction and draw it; it may act by repulsion and repel it; it may act as a sort of little spirit and fly away with it. In all these cases it *acts*. The more it acts, the more effect it has. In double the time it produces double the motion. If the mass is big, it takes more force to make the mass move; if the mass of the body is small, it is moved more easily. Therefore when we want to measure a force in this way we do not press it against springs to see how much it will press them in. What we do is to cause it to act on bodies that are free to move and see what motions it will produce in them. Of course we can only do this with things that are free to move. You cannot treat force in this way if you have only a pair of scales; in that case you would have to be content with simply measuring pressures. It is important clearly to grasp this idea. If a body has a certain mass, then the force acting on it is measured by the amount of motion that will in a given time be imparted to that mass, provided that the mass is free to move. This is to be our definition of force.

Therefore, by the action of an attraction or any other force on a body free to move; motion is continually being imparted to the body. Motion is, as it were, poured into it, and therefore the body continually moves faster and faster.

Here is a ball flying through the air. Let us suppose that forces are acting on it. How can we measure them? We cannot feel what pressures are being exerted on it. The only thing we can do is to watch its motions, and see how it flies. If it goes more and more quickly, we say, "There is propelling force acting on it"; if it begins to stop, we say again, "There is retarding force acting on it." So long as it does not change its speed or direction, we say, "There is no force acting on it." By this method, therefore, we tell whether a body is being acted on by force, simply by observing its speed or its change of speed. Merely to say a body is *moving* does not tell us that force is acting on it. All we know is that, if it is moving, force *has* acted on it. It is only when we see it changing its speed or direction, that is changing its motion, that we say *force* is acting. Every change of motion, either in direction or speed, must be the result of force, and must be proportional to that force. This is what we mean when we say motion is the test and measure of force.

This most interesting way of looking at the
matter lies at the root of the whole theory of
mechanics. It is the foundation of the system which
the stupendous genius of Newton conceived in order
to explain the motion of the sun, moon, and stars.

Forces were treated by him as proportional to
the motions, and the motions proportional to the
forces, and with this idea he solved a part of the
riddle of the universe. Galileo had partly seen the
same thing, but he never saw it so clearly as
Newton. Great discoveries are only made by seeing
things clearly. What required the force of a genius
in one age to see in the next may be understood by
a child.

Hence then we say a force is that which in a given
time produces a given motion in a given mass which
is free to move.

You must have time for a force to act in; for
however great the force, in no time there can be
no motion. You must have mass for a force to
act on; no mass, no effect. You must have free
space for the mass to move in; no freedom to move,
no movement.

But what is this "mass"? We do not know;
it is a mystery. We call it "quantity of matter."
In uniform substances it varies with size. Double
the volume, double the mass. Cut a cake in half,
each half has the same "mass." But then is mass
"weight"? No, it is not. *Weight* is the action of

the earth's attraction on matter. No earth to attract, and you would have no weight, but you would still have " mass." What then is matter ? Of that we have no idea. The greatest minds are now at work upon it. But *mass* is quantity of matter. Knock a brick against your head, and you will know what mass is. It is not the weight of the brick that gives you a bump ; it is the mass. Try to throw a ball of lead, and you will know what mass is. Try to push a heavy waggon, and you will know what mass is. *Weights*, that is earth attractions on masses, are proportional to the masses at the same place. This, as we have seen, is known by experiment.

Therefore, when a force acts for a certain time on a mass that is free to move, however small the force and however small the time, that body will move. When a baby in a temper stamps upon the earth it makes the earth move—not much, it is true, but still it moves ; nay, more, in theory, not a fly can jump into the air without moving the earth and the whole solar system. Only, as you may imagine they do not show it appreciably. Still, in theory the motion is there.

Hence then there are two different ways of considering and estimating forces, one suitable for observations on bodies at rest, the other suitable for observations of bodies that are free to move. The force of course always tends to produce motion. If, however, motion is impossible, then it develops pressures which we can measure, and calculate, and observe. If the body is free to move, then the force produces motions which we can also measure, calculate, and observe. And we can compare these two sets of effects. We can say, " A force which, acting on a ball of a mass of one pound, would produce such and such motions, would if it acted on a certain spring produce so much compression."

The attraction of the earth on masses of matter that are not free to move gives rise to forces which are called weights. Thus the attraction of gravitation on a mass of one pound produces a pressure equal to a weight of one pound. Unfortunately the same word " pound " is used to express both the mass and the weight, and has come down to us from days when the nature of mass was not very well appreciated. But great care must be taken not to confuse these two meanings.

But the earth's attractions and all other forces acting upon matter which is free to move give rise to changes of motion. The word used for a change of motion is " acceleration " or a quickening. " He accelerated his pace," we say. That is, he quickened it ; he added to his motion. So that *force*, acting on *mass* during a *time*, produces acceleration.

From this, then, it follows that if a force continues to act on a body the body keeps moving quicker and quicker. When the force stops acting, the motion already acquired goes on, but the acceleration stops. That is to say, the body goes on moving in a straight line uniformly at the pace it had when the force stopped.

If, then, a body is exposed to the action of a force, and held tight, what will happen ? It will, of course, remain fixed. Now let it go—it will then, being a free body, begin to move. As long as the force acts, the force keeps putting more and more motion into the body, like pouring water into a jug, the longer you pour the faster the motion becomes. The body keeps all the motion it had, and keeps adding all the motion it gains. It is like a boy saving up his weekly pocket-money : he has what he had, and he keeps adding to that. So if in one second a motion is imparted of one foot a second, then in another second a motion of one foot a second more will be added, making together a motion of two feet a second ; in another second of force action the motion will have been increased or " accelerated " by another foot per second, and so on. The speed will thus be always proportional to the force and the time. If we write the letter V to represent the motion, or speed, or velocity; F to represent the acceleration or gain of motion ; and T to represent the time, then $V = FT$. Here V is the velocity the body will have acquired at the end of the time T, if free to move and submitted to a force capable of producing an acceleration of F feet per second in a unit of time.

V is the final velocity. The average velocity will
be $\frac{1}{2}$ V, for it began with no velocity and increased
uniformly. How far will the body have fallen in
the interval? Manifestly we get that by multiplying the time by the average velocity, that is
S = $\frac{1}{2}$ V T, where V, as I said, is the final velocity,
but we found that V = F T. Hence by substitution
S = $\frac{1}{2}$ F T × T = $\frac{1}{2}$ F T².

It is to be carefully borne in mind that these
letters V, S, and T do not represent velocities,
spaces, and times, but merely represent arith-
metical numbers of units of velocities, spaces,
and times. Thus V represents V feet per second,
S represents S feet, and T represents T seconds.
And when we use the equation V = F T we do
not mean that by multiplying a force by a
time you can produce a velocity. If, for instance,
it be true that you can obtain the number of
inhabitants (H) in London by multiplying the
average number of persons (P) who live in a house
by the number of houses (N), this may be expressed
by the equation H = P N. But this does not
mean that by multiplying people into houses you
can produce inhabitants. H, P, and N are numbers of units, and they are *numbers only.*

Therefore when a body is being acted on by an
accelerating force it tends to go faster and faster as
it proceeds, and therefore its velocity increases with
the time. But the space passed through increases

faster still, for as the time runs on not only does the space passed through increase, but the rate of passing also gets bigger. It goes on increasing at an increasing rate. It is like a man who has an increasing income and always goes on saving it. His total mounts up not merely in proportion to the time, but the very rate of increase also increases with the time, so that the total increase is in proportion to the time multiplied into the time, in other words to the square of the time. So then, if I let a body drop from rest under the action of any force capable of producing an acceleration, the space passed through will be as the square of the time.

Now let us see what the speed will be if the force is gravity, that is the attraction of the earth.

Turning back to what was said about Galileo, it will be remembered that he showed that all bodies, big and small, light and heavy, fell to the earth at the same speeds. What is that speed? Let us denominate by G the number of feet per second of increase of motion produced in a body by the earth's action during one second. Then the velocity at the end of that second will be $V = G T$. The space fallen through will be $S = \frac{1}{2} G T^2$.

What I want to know then is this: how far will a body under the action of gravity fall in a second of time?

This, of course, is a matter for measurement. If we can get a machine to measure seconds, we shall

be able to do it; but inasmuch as falling bodies
begin by falling sixteen feet in the first second and
afterwards go on falling quicker and quicker, the
measurements are difficult. Galileo wanted to see
if he could make it easier to observe. He said to
himself, " If I can only water down the force of
gravity and make it weaker, so that the body will

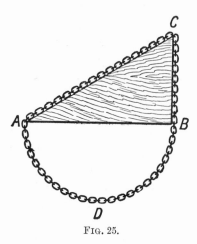

FIG. 25.

move very slowly
under its action,
then the time of
falling will be
easier to ob-
serve." But how
to do it? This
is one of those
things the dis-
covery of which
at once marks
the inventor.
    The idea of
Galileo was, in-
stead of letting the body drop vertically, to make
it roll slowly down an incline, for a body put upon
an incline is not urged down the incline with the
same force which tends to make it fall vertically.

    Can any law be discovered tending to show what
the force is with which gravity tends to drag a mass
down an incline ?

    There is a simple one, and before Galileo's time

it had been discovered by Stevinus, an engineer.
Stevinus' solution was as follows. Suppose that
ABC is a wedge-shaped block of wood. Let a loop
of heavy chain be hung over it, and suppose that
there is a little pulley at C and no friction any-
where. Then the chain will hang at rest. But the
lower part, from A to B, is symmetrical; that is to
say, it is even in shape on both sides. Hence, so far
as any pull it exerts is concerned, the half from
A to D will balance the other half from B to D.
Therefore, like weights in a scale, you may remove
both, and then the force of gravity acting down the
plane on the part AC will balance the force of
gravity acting vertically on the part CB. Now the
weight of any part of the chain, since it is uniform,
is proportional to its length. Hence, then, the
gravitational force down the plane of a piece
whose weight equals CA is equal to the gravitational force vertically of a piece whose weight
equals CB. In other words, the force of gravity
acting down a plane is diminished in the ratio of
CB to CA.

But when a body falls vertically, then, as we
have seen, $S = \frac{1}{2} G T^2$, where S is the space it
will fall through, G the number of feet per second
of velocity that gravity, acting vertically on a body,
will produce in it in a second, and T the number of
seconds of time. If then, instead of falling vertically, the body is to fall obliquely down a plane,

T.C.   G

instead of G we must put as the accelerating force

$$G \times \frac{\text{vertical height of the end of the plane}}{\text{length of the plane}}.$$

To try the experiment, he took a beam of wood thirty-six feet long with a groove in it. He inclined it so that one end was one foot higher than the other. Hence the acceleration down the plane was $\frac{1}{36}$ G, where G is the vertical acceleration due to gravity which he wanted to discover. Then he measured the time a brass ball took to run down the plane thirty-six feet long, and found it to be nine seconds. Whence from the equation given above 36 feet $= \frac{1}{2}$ acceleration of gravity down the plane $\times$ (9 seconds)^2. Whence it follows that the acceleration of gravity down the plane is $\frac{36 \times 2}{(9)^2}$ feet per second.

But the slope of the plane is one thirty-sixth to the vertical. Therefore the vertical acceleration of gravity, *i.e.*, the velocity which gravity would induce in a vertical direction in a second, is equal to thirty-six times that which it exercises down the plane, *i.e.*,

$$36 \times \frac{36 \times 2}{(9)^2};$$ and this equals 32 feet per second.

Though this method is ingenious, it possesses two defects. One is the error produced by friction, the other from failure to observe that the force of gravity on the ball is not only exerted in getting it

down the plane, but also in rotating it, and for this
no allowance has been made.   The allowance to be
made for rotation is complicated, and involves more
knowledge than Galileo possessed.   Still the result
is approximately true.

The next attempt to measure G, that is the
velocity that gravity will produce on a body in a
second of time, was made by Attwood, a Cambridge
professor.   His idea was to weaken the force
of gravity and thus make the
action slow, not by making it act
obliquely, but by allowing it to act,
not on the whole, but only on a portion of the mass to be moved.   For
this purpose he hung two equal
weights over a very delicately constructed pulley.   Gravity, of course,
could not act on these, for any effect

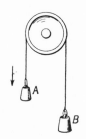

Fig. 26.

it produced on one would be negatived by its effect
on the other.   The weights would therefore remain
at rest.   If, however, a small weight W, equal say
to a hundredth of the combined weight of the weights
A and B and W, were suddenly put on A, then it
would descend under an accelerating force equal to
a hundredth part of ordinary gravity.   We should
then have

$$\text{S (the space moved through by the weights)} = \tfrac{1}{2} \times \frac{G}{100} \times t^2.$$

With such a system, he found that in $7\tfrac{1}{2}$ seconds the weights moved through 9 feet. Whence he got

$$9 = \tfrac{1}{2}\frac{G}{100} \times (7\tfrac{1}{2})^2.$$

From which

$$G = \frac{2 \times 9 \times 100}{(7\tfrac{1}{2})^2} = 32 \text{ feet per second nearly.}$$

Thus by letting gravity only act on a hundredth part of the total weight moved, namely A, B, and W, he weakened its action 100 times, and thus made the time of falling and the space fallen through sufficiently large to be capable of measurement. To sum up, when a body free to move is acted upon by the force of gravity, its speed will increase in proportion to the time it has been acted upon, and the space it will pass through from rest is proportional to the square of the time during which the accelerating force has acted on it.

Gravity is, of course, not the only accelerating force with which we are acquainted. If a spring be suddenly allowed to act on a body and pull it, the body begins to move, and its action is gradually accelerated, just as though it were attracted, and the acceleration of its motion will be proportional to the time during which the accelerating force acts. Similarly, if gunpowder be exploded in a gun-barrel, and the force thus produced be allowed to act on a bullet, the motion of the bullet is accelerated so long as it is in the barrel. When the bullet leaves the barrel it goes on with a uniform pace in a

straight line, which, however, by the earth's attraction is at once deflected into a curve, and altered
by the resistance of the air.

It has been already stated that motions may be
considered independently one of another, so that if
a body be exposed to two different forces the action
of these forces can be considered and calculated
each independently of the other.   Let us take an
example of this law.   We have seen if a body
is propelled forwards, and then the force acting
on it ceases, that
it proceeds on
with uniform un-
changing velo-
city, and if no-
thing impeded it,

FIG. 27.

or influenced it, it would go on in a straight line at
a uniform speed.

We have also seen that if a body is exposed to
the action of an accelerating force such as gravity
it constantly keeps being accelerated, it constantly
keeps gaining motion, and its speed becomes quicker
and quicker.

Let us suppose a body exposed to both of these
forces at the same time.   Shoot it out of a cannon,
and let an accelerating force act on it, not in the
direction it is going, but in some other direction,
say at right angles.   What will happen?   In the
direction in which it is going, its speed will remain

uniform.   In the direction in which the accelerating
force is acting, it will move faster and faster.   Thus
along *A B* it will proceed uniformly.   If it proceeded
uniformly also along *A C* (as it would do if a simple
force acted on it and then ceased to act), then as a
result it would go in the oblique line *A D*, the
obliquity being determined by the relative magni-
tude of the forces acting on it.   But how if it went
uniformly along *A B*, but at an accelerated pace
along *A C*?   Then while in equal times the distances
along *A B* would be uniform the distances in the

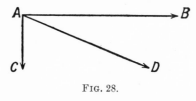

same times along
A C would be
getting bigger
and bigger.   It
*would not describe
a straight line; it*

FIG. 28.

would go in a curve.   This is very interesting.   Let
us take an example of it.   Suppose we give a ball a
blow horizontally; as soon as it quits the bat it
would of course go on horizontally in a straight
line at a uniform speed; but now if I at the same
instant expose it to the accelerating force of gravity,
then, of course, while its horizontal movement will
go on uniformly, its downward drop will keep
increasing at a speed varying as the time.   And
while the total distances horizontally will be uniform
in equal times, the total downward drop from *A B*
will be as the squares of the times.   Here, then,

you have a point moving uniformly in a horizontal direction, but as the squares of the times in a vertical direction. It describes a curve. What curve? Why, one whose distances go uniformly one way, but increase as the squares the other way.

This interesting curve is called a parabola. With a ball simply hit by a bat, the motion is so very fast that we cannot see it well. Cannot we make it go slowly? Let us remember what Galileo did. He used an inclined plane to water down his force of gravity. Let us do the same. Let us take an inclined plane and throw on

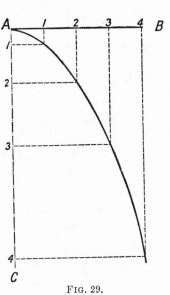

FIG. 29.

it a ball horizontally. It will go in a curve. Its speed is uniform horizontally, but is accelerated downwards. If we desire to trace the curve it is easy to do. We coat the ball with cloth and then dip it in the inkpot. It will then describe a visible parabola. If I tilt up the plane and make the force of gravity big, the parabola is long and thin;

if I weaken down the force of gravity by making
the plane nearly horizontal, then it is wide and
flat.

One can also show this by a stream of peas or
shot. The little bullets go each with a uniform
velocity horizontally, and an accelerated force
downwards.

Instead of peas we can use water. A stream of
it rushing horizontally out of an orifice will soon
bend down into a parabola.

Thus then I have tried to show what force is
and how it is measured. I repeat again, when a
body is free to move, then, if no further force acts on
it, it will go on in a straight line at a uniform speed,
but if a force continues to act on it in any direction,
then that force produces in each unit of time a unit
of acceleration in the direction in which the force
acts, and the result is that the body goes on moving
towards the direction of acceleration at a constantly
increasing speed, and hence passing over spaces
that are greater and greater as the speed increases.
This is the notion of a "force." In all that has
been said above it has been assumed that the
attraction of gravity on a body does not increase as
that body gets nearer to the earth. This is not
strictly true; in reality the attractive force of
gravity increases as the earth's centre is approached.
But small distances through which the weights in
Attwood's machine fall make no appreciable

difference, being as nothing compared to the radius of earth. For practical purposes, therefore, the force may be considered uniform on bodies that are being moved within a few feet of the earth's surface. It is only when we have to consider the motions of the planets that considerations of the change of attractive force due to distance have to be considered.

I am glad to say that the most tiresome, or rather the most difficult, part of our inquiry is now over. With the help of the notions already acquired, we are now ready to get to the pendulum, and to show how it came about that a boy who once in church amused himself by watching the swinging of the great lamps instead of attending to the service laid the foundation of our modern methods of measuring time.

CHAPTER III.

We have examined the action of a body under the accelerating or speed-quickening force due to gravity, the attractive force of which on any body is always proportional to the mass of that body. Let us now consider another form of acceleration.

Take the case of a strip of indiarubber. If pulled it resists and tends to spring back. The more I pull it out the harder is the pull I have to exert. This is true of all springs. It is true of spiral springs, whether they are pulled out or pushed in, and in each case the amount by which the spring is pulled out or pushed in is proportional to the pressure. This law is called Hooke's law. It was expressed by him in Latin, "Ut tensio, sic vis" : "As the extension, so the force." It is true of all elastic bodies, and it is true whether they are pulled out or pushed in or bent aside. The common spring balance is devised on this principle. The body to be weighed is hung on a hook suspended from a spring. The amount by which the spring is

Fig. 30.

pulled out is a measure of the weight of the body. If you take a fishing rod and put the butt end of it on a table and secure it by putting something heavy on the end, then the tip will bend down on account of its own weight. Mark the point to which it goes. Now, if you hang a weight on the tip, the tip will bend down a little further. If you put double the weight the tip will go down double the distance, and so on until the fishing rod is considerably bent, so that its form is altered and a new law of flexure comes into play. Suppose I use a spring as an accelerating force.

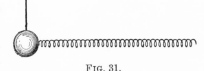

FIG. 31.

For example, suppose I suspend a heavy ball by a string and then attach a spiral spring to it and pull the spring aside. The ball will be drawn after the spring. If then I let the ball go, it will begin to move. The force of the spring will act upon it as an accelerating force, and the ball will go on moving quicker and quicker. But the acceleration will not be like that of gravity. There will be two differences. The pull of the spring will in no way depend on the mass of the ball, and the pull of the spring, instead of being constant, like the pull of gravity,

will become weaker and weaker as the ball
yields to it.   Consequently the equations above
given which determine the relations between this
space passed through, the velocity, and the time
which were determined in the case of gravity are
no longer true, and a different set of relations has
to be determined.   This can be easily done by
mathematics.   But I do not propose to go into it.

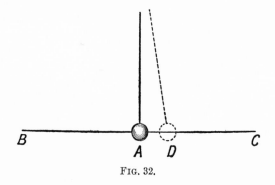

FIG. 32.

I prefer to offer a rough and ready explanation,
which, though it does not amount to a proof, yet
enables us to accept the truth that can be established both by experiment and by calculation.

Let a heavy ball (A) be suspended by a long
string, so that the action of gravity sideways on the
ball is very small and may be neglected, and to
each side attach an indiarubber thread fastened at
B and C.   Then when the ball is pulled aside a
little, say to a position D, it will tend to fly back to

A with a force proportioned to the distance $A\ D$. What will be the time it will take to do this? If the distance $A\ D$ is small, the ball has only a small distance to go, but then, on the other hand, it has only small forces acting on it. If the distance $A\ D$ is bigger, then it has a longer distance to go, but larger forces to urge it. These counteract one another, so that the time in each case will be the same.

The question is this:—Will you go a long distance with a powerful horse, or a small distance with a weak horse? If the distance in each case is proportioned to the power of the horse, then the amount of the distance does not matter. The powerful horse goes the long distance in the same time that the weak horse goes the short distance. And so it is here. However far you pull out the spring, the accelerative pull on the ball is proportioned to the distance. But the time of pulling the ball in depends on the distance. So that each neutralises the other. Whence then we have this most important fact, that springs are all isochronous; that is to say, any body attached to any spring whatever, whether it is big or small, straight or curly, long or short, has a time of vibration quite independent of the bigness of the vibration. The experiment is easy to try with a ball mounted on a long arm that can swing horizontally. It is attached on each side to an elastic thread. If pulled aside, it vibrates, but observe, the vibration is exactly the same whether the bigness of the vibration is great or small. If the pull aside is big, the force of restitution is big; if the pull is small, the force of restitution is small. In one case the ball has a longer distance to go, but

then at all points of its path it has a proportionally stronger force to pull it; if the ball has a smaller distance to go, then at all the corresponding points of its path it has a proportionally weaker force to pull it. Thus the time remains the same whether you have the powerful horse for the long journey or the weaker horse for the smaller journey.

Next take a short, stiff spring of steel. One of the kind known as tuning forks may be employed.

FIG. 33.

The reader is probably aware that sounds are produced by very rapid pulsations of the air. Any series of taps becomes a continuous sound if it is only rapid enough. For example, if I tap a card at the rate of 264 times in a second, I should get a continuous sound such as that given by the middle C note of the piano. That, in fact, is the rate at which the piano string is vibrating when C is struck, and that vibration it is that gives the taps to the air by which the note is produced.

This can be very easily proved. For if you lift up the end of a bicycle and cause the driving wheel to spin pretty rapidly by turning the pedal with the hand, then the wheel will rotate perhaps about three times in a second. If a visiting card be held so as to be flipped by the spokes as they fly by, since there are about thirty-six of them, we should get a series of taps at the rate of about 108 a second. This on trial will be found to nearly correspond to the note A, the lowest space on the bass clef of music. As the speed of rotation is lowered, the tone of the note becomes lower; if the speed is made greater, the pitch of the note becomes higher, and the note more shrill. However far or near the card is held from the centre of the wheel makes no difference, for the number of taps per second remains the same. So, again, if a bit of watch-spring be rapidly drawn over a file, you hear a musical note. The finer the file, and the more rapid the action, the higher the note. The action of a tuning fork and of a vibrating string in producing a note depends simply on the beating of the air. The hum of insects is also similarly produced by the rapid flapping of their wings.

It is an experimental fact that when a piano note is struck, as the vibration gradually ceases the sound dies away, but the pitch of the note remains unchanged. A tune played softly, so that the strings vibrate but little, remains the same tune still, and with the same pitch for the notes.

A "siren" is an ingenious apparatus for producing a series of very rapid puffs of air. It consists of a small wheel with oblique holes in it, mounted so as to revolve in close proximity to a fixed wheel with similar holes in it. If air be forced through the wheels, by reason of the obliquity of the orifices in the movable wheel it is caused to rotate. As it does so, the air is alternately interrupted and allowed to pass, so that a series of very rapid puffs is produced. As the air is forced in, the wheel turns faster and faster. The rapidity of succession of the puffs increases so that the note produced by them gradually increases in pitch till it rises to a sort of scream. For steamers these "sirens" are worked by steam, and make a very loud noise.

It is, however, impossible to make a tuning fork or a stretched piano spring alter the pitch of its note without altering the elastic force of the spring by altering its tension, or without putting weights on the arms of the tuning fork to make it go more slowly. And this is because the tuning fork and the piano spring, being elastic, obey Hooke's law, " As the deflection, so the force "; and therefore the time of back spring is in each case invariable, and the pitch of the note produced therefore remains invariable, whatever the amplitude of the vibration may be.

Upon this law depends the correct going of both clocks and watches.

Wonderful nature, that causes the uniformity of sounds of a piano, or a violin, to depend on the same laws that govern the uniform going of a watch! Nay, more, all creation is vibrating. The surge of the sea upon the coast that swishes in at regular intervals, the colours of light, which consist of ripples made in an elastic ether, which springs back with a restitutional force proportioned to its displacement, all depend upon the same law. This grand law by which so many phenomena of nature are governed has a very beautiful name, which I hope you will remember. It is called "harmonic motion," by which is meant that when the atoms of nature vibrate they vibrate, like piano strings, according to the laws of harmony. The ancient Pythagorean philosophers thought that all nature moved to music, and that dying souls could begin to hear the tones to which the stars moved in their orbits. They called it, as you know, the music of the spheres. But could they have seen what science has revealed to man's patient efforts, they would have seen a vision of harmony in which not a ray of light, not a string of a musical instrument, not a pipe of an organ, not an undulation of all-pervading electricity, not

T.C.   H

a wing of a fly, but vibrates according to the law of harmony, the simple easy law of which a boy's catapult is the type, and which, as we have seen, teaches us that when an elastic body is displaced the force of restitution, in other words, the force tending to restore it to its old position, is proportional to the displacement, and the time of vibration is uniform. The last is the important thing for us; we seem to get a gleam of a notion of how the clock and watch problem is going to be solved.

But before we get to that we have yet to go back a little.

About the year 1580 an inattentive youth (it was our friend Galileo again) watched the swing of one of the great chandeliers in the cathedral church at Pisa. The chandeliers have been renewed since his day, it was one of the old lamps that he watched. It had been lit, and allowed to swing through a considerable space. He expected that as it gradually came to rest it would swing in a quicker and quicker time, but it seemed to be uniform. This was curious. He wanted to measure the time of its swing. For this purpose he counted his pulse-beats. So far as he could judge, there were exactly the same number in each pendulum swing.

This greatly interested him, and at home he began to try some experiments. As he got older his attention was repeatedly turned to that subject, and he finally established in a satisfactory way the law that, if a weight is hung to the end of a string and caused to vibrate, it is isochronous, or equal-timed, no matter what the extent of the arc of vibration.

The first use of this that he made was to make a little machine with a string of which you could vary the length, for use by doctors. For the doctors of that day had no gold watch to pull out while with solemn face they watched the ticks. They were delighted with the new invention, and for years doctors used to take out the little string and weight, and put one hand on the patient's pulse while they adjusted the string till the pendulum beat in unison with the pulse. By observing the length of the string, they were then able to tell how many beats the pulse made in a minute. But Galileo did not stop there. He proceeded to examine the laws which govern the pendulum.

We will follow these investigations, which will largely depend on what we have already learned.

Before, however, it is possible to understand the laws which govern the pendulum, there are one or two simple matters connected with the balance and operation of forces which have to be grasped.

Suppose that we have a flat piece of wood of any shape like Fig. 34, and that we put a screw through any spot *A* in it, no matter where, and screw it to a wall, so that it can turn round the screw as round a pivot.

Next we will knock a tintack into any point *B*,

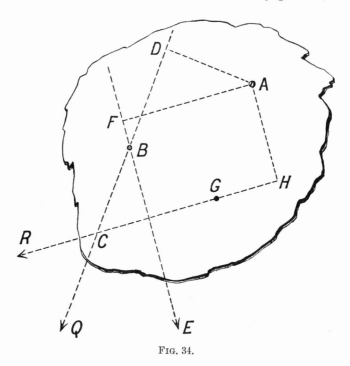

Fig. 34.

and tie a string on to *B*. Then if I pull at the string in any direction *B C* the board tends to twist round the screw at *A*. What will the strength of the twisting force be? It will depend on the

strength of the pull, and on the " leverage," or
distance of the line $C\,B$ from A. We might imagine
the string, instead of being attached at B, to be
attached at D; then, if I put P as the strength
of the pull, the twisting power would be represented by $P \times A\,D$. This is called the " moment "
of the force P round
the centre A. It
would be the same
as if I had simply
an arm $A\,D$, and
pulled upon it with
the force P. It is an
experimental truth,
known to the old
Greek philosophers,
that moments, or
twisting powers, are
equal when in each
case the result of
multiplying the arm
by the power acting at right angles to it is
equal.

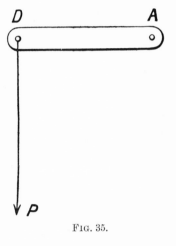

Fig. 35.

Now suppose $A\,B$ is a pendulum, with a bob
B of 10 lbs. weight, and suppose it has been
drawn aside out of the vertical so that the bob is
in the position B. Then the weight of the bob will
act vertically downwards along the line $B\,C$. The
moment, or twisting power, of the weight will be

equal to 10 lbs. multiplied by AD, AD being a line perpendicular to BC.

Now suppose that another string were tied to the bob B, and pulled in a direction at right angles to AB, with a force P just enough to hold the bob back in the position B. The pull along $DB \times AB$ would be the moment of that pull round the point

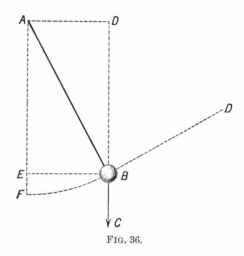

FIG. 36.

A. But, because this moment just holds the pendulum up, it follows that the moment of the weight of the pendulum round A is equal to the moment of the pull of the string BD round A.

Whence $P \times AB = 10$ lbs. $\times AD$.

Whence $P = 10$ lbs. $\times \dfrac{AD}{AB}$.

But $A B$ is always the same, whatever the side deflection or displacement of the pendulum may be. Whence then we see that when a pendulum is pulled aside a distance $E B$ (which is always equal to $A D$), then the force tending to bring it back to E is always proportional to $E B$. But if the pendulum be fairly long, say $39\frac{1}{7}$ inches, and the displacement $E B$ be small,—in other words, if we do not drag it much out of the vertical,—then we may say that the force tending to bring it back to F, its position of rest, is not very different from the force tending to bring it back to E. But $F B$ is the "displacement" of the pendulum, and, therefore, we find that when a pendulum is displaced, or deflected, or pulled aside a little, the amount of the deflection is always very nearly proportional to the force which was used to produce the deflection. This important law can be verified by experiment. If C is a small pulley, and $B C$ a string attached to a pendulum $A B$ whose bob is B. Then if a weight D be tied to the string and passed over a pulley C, the amount $F B$ by which the weight D will deflect the bob B is almost exactly proportional to D, so long as we only make the deflection $E B$ small, that is two or three inches, where say $39\frac{1}{7}$ inches is the length $A B$ of the pendulum.

If $F B$ is made too big, then the line $B F$ can no longer be considered nearly equal to the arc of deflection $E B$, and the proposition is no longer true.

Hence then, both by experiment and on theory, we find that for small distances the displacement of a pendulum bob is approximately equal to the force by which that displacement is produced.

But if so, then from what has gone before, we have an example of harmonic motion. The weight of the bob, tending to pull the bob back to *E*, acts just as an elastic band would act, that is to say pulls more strongly in proportion as the distance *F B* is bigger. In fact, if we could remove the force of gravity still leaving the mass *B* of the pendulum bob, the force of an elastic band acting so as to tend to pull the bob back to rest might be used to replace it. It would be all one whether the bob were brought back to rest by the downward force of its own gravity, or by the horizontal force of a properly arranged elastic band of suitable length.

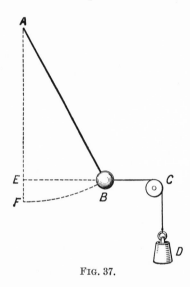

FIG. 37.

But the motion of the bob, under the influence

of the pull of an elastic band where the strain was always proportional to the displacement, would, as we have seen, be harmonic motion, and performed in equal times whatever the extent of the swing. Whence then we conclude that if the swings of a pendulum are not too big, say not exceeding two and a half inches each way, the motion may be considered harmonic motion, and the swings will be made in equal times whether they are large or small ones. In other words, a clock with a $39\frac{1}{7}$ inch pendulum and side swing on each side if not over two inches will keep time, whatever the arc of swing may be.

This may be verified experimentally. Take a pendulum of wood $39\frac{1}{7}$ inches long, and affix to its end a bob of 10 lbs. weight. The pendulum will swing once in each second. To pull it aside two inches we should want a weight such that its moment about the point of support was equal to the moment of the force of gravity acting on the bob, about the point of support. In other words, the weight required $\times 39\frac{1}{7}$ inches = 10 lbs. $\times$ 2 inches. Whence the weight required = $\frac{1}{2}$ lb. (nearly).

Now fix a similar pendulum $A\,B$ $39\frac{1}{2}$ inches long, horizontally, with a weight B of 10 lbs. on it. Fasten it to a vertical shaft $C\,D$, with a tie rod of wire or string $A\,B$ so as to keep it up, and attach to each side of the rod $A\,B$ elastic threads $E\,F$ and $E\,G$.

Let these threads be tied on at such a point that when *B* is pulled aside two inches the force tending to bring it back to rest is half a pound. Then if set vibrating the rod will swing backwards and forwards in equal times, no matter how big, the arc of vibration (provided the arc is kept small), and the time of oscillation will be that of a pendulum, namely, one

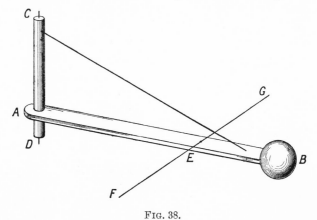

Fig. 38.

swing in a second. In fact, whether you put *A B* vertically and let it swing on the pivots *C* and *D* by the force of gravity, or put it horizontally, and thus prevent gravity acting on it, but make it swing under the accelerating influence of a pair of elastic bands so arranged as to be equivalent to gravity, in each case it will swing in seconds.

It is this curious property of the circle that makes the vertical force of gravity on a pendulum pull it as though it were a horizontally acting elastic band ; that is the reason why a pendulum is equal-time-swinging, or, as it is called, isochronous, from two Greek words that mean " the same " and " time."

But it must be remembered that this equal swinging is only approximate, and only true when the arc of vibration is small.

Here then we have a proof which shows us that the pendulum of a clock and the balance wheel of a watch depend on exactly the same principles. They are each an example of harmonic motion.

The next question that arises is whether the weight of the pendulum has any influence upon the time of its vibration.

A little reflection will soon convince us that it has none. For we know that the time that bodies take to fall to the ground under the action of gravity is independent of the weight. A falling 2 lb. weight is only equivalent to two pound-weights falling side by side.

In the same way and by the same reasoning we might take two pendulums of equal length, and each with a bob weighing 1 lb. They would, if put side by side close together swing in equal times. But the time would be the same if they were fastened together, and made into one pendulum.

For inasmuch as the fall of a pendulum is due

to gravity, and the action of gravity upon a body is proportional to its mass, it follows that in a pendulum the part of the gravitational force that acts upon each part of the mass is occupied in moving that mass, and the whole pendulum may be considered as a bundle of pendulums tied together and vibrating together.

The same would be the case with a pendulum vibrating under the influence of a spring. If you have two bobs and two springs, they will vibrate in the same time as one bob accelerated by one spring. In this case, however, the force of the one spring must be equal to the combined force of the two springs. In other words, the springs must be made proportional in strength to the masses.

Hence, then, you cannot increase the speed of the vibration of a pendulum by adding weight to the bob.

On the other hand, if you have a bob vibrating under the influence of a spring, like the balance wheel of a watch, then if you increase the bob without increasing the spring, since the mass to be moved has increased without a corresponding increase in the accelerating force acting on it, the time of swing will alter accordingly.

But in the case of gravity, by altering the mass, you thereby proportionally alter the attraction on it, and therefore the time of swing is unaltered.

The explanation which has been given above of the reasons why a pendulum swings backwards and forwards in a given time independently of the length of the arc through which it swings, that is to say of the amount by which it sways from side to side, is only approximate, because in the proof we assumed that the arc of swing and the line FB were equal, which is not really and exactly true. Galileo never got at the real solution, though he tried hard. It was reserved for another than he to find the true path of an iso-chronous pen-dulum and completely to determine its

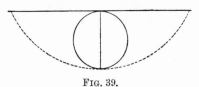

FIG. 39.

laws. Huygens, a Dutch mathematician, found that the true path in which a pendulum ought to swing if it is to be really isochronous is a curve called a cycloid, that is to say the curve which is traced out by a pencil fixed on the rim of a hoop when the hoop is rolled along a straight ruler. It is the curve which a nail sticking out of the rim of a waggon wheel would scratch upon a wall. I will not go into the mathematical proof of this. Clocks are not made with cycloidal pendulums, because when the arc of a pendulum is small the swing is so very near a cycloid as to make no appreciable difference in time-keeping.

I am now glad to be able to say that I have dealt
with all the mathematics that is necessary to enable
the mechanism of a clock to be understood.   It all
leads up to this:—

(1) A harmonic motion is one in which the
accelerating force increases with the distance of
the body from some fixed point.

(2) Bodies moving harmonically make their
swings about this point in equal times.

(3) A spring of any sort or shape always has a
restitutional force proportional to the displacement.

(4) And therefore masses attached to springs
vibrate in equal times however large the vibration
may be.

(5) The bob of a pendulum, oscillating backwards
and forwards, acts like a weight under the
influence of a spring, and is therefore isochronous.

(6) The time of vibration of a pendulum is
uninfluenced by changes in the weight of the bob,
but is influenced by changes in the length of the
pendulum rod.   The time of vibration of a mass
attached to a spring is influenced by changes in
the mass.

We have now to deal with the application of
these principles to clocks and watches.

Clocks had been known before the time of
Galileo, and before the invention of the pendulum.
They had what is known as balance, or verge
escapements.   Strictly in order of time I ought to

explain them here. But I will not do so. I will go
on to describe the pendulum clock, and then I will
go back and explain the verge escapement, which,
we shall see, is really a sort of huge watch of a
very imperfect character.

As soon as Galileo had discovered that pendulums
were isochronous, that is, equi-time-swinging, he
set to work to see whether he could not contrive
to make a timepiece by means of them. This
would be easy if only he could keep a pendulum
swinging. When a pendulum is set swinging, it
soon comes to rest. What brings it to rest? The
resistance of the air and the friction of the pivots.
Therefore what is obviously wanted is something
to give it a kick now and then, but the thing
must kick with discretion. If it kicked at the
wrong time, it might actually stop the pendulum
instead of keeping it going. You want something
that, just as the pendulum is at one end and has
begun to move, will give it a further push. Suppose
that I have a swing and that I put a boy in it,
and I swing him to and fro. I time my pushes.
As he comes back against my hand I let him
push it back, and then just as the swing turns I
give it a further push. But I cannot stand doing
that all day. I must make a machine to do it.
Now what sort of a machine?

First, the machine must have a reservoir of
force. I can't get a machine to do work unless I

wind it up, nor a man to do work unless I feed him, which is his way of being wound up. But then what do I want him to do? I want him, when I give him a push, to push me back harder. I want a reservoir of force such that when a pendulum comes back and touches it, the touch, like the pressure of the trigger of a gun, shall allow some pent-up power to escape and to drive the pendulum forward.

This is the case in a swing. Each time that the swing returns to my hands I give it a push, which serves to sustain the motion that would otherwise be destroyed by friction and the resistance of the air.

Such an arrangement, if it can be contrived mechanically, is called an "escapement."

An arrangement of this kind was contrived by Galileo. He provided a wheel, as is here shown, with a number of pins round it. The pendulum $A B$ has an arm $A H$ attached to it, and there is a ratchet $C D$ which engages with the pins. The ratchet has a projecting arm $E F$.

When the pendulum comes back towards the end of its beat, the arm $A H$ strikes the arm $E F$, and raises the ratchet $C D$. This releases the wheel, which has a weight wound up upon it, and therefore at once tries to go round. The consequence is, that the pin G strikes upon the arm $A H$, and thus on its return stroke gives an impetus

to the pendulum. As the pin *G* moves forward it
slides on the arm *A H* till it slips over the point *H*.
The wheel now being free, would fly round were
it not that when the pendulum returned, and the

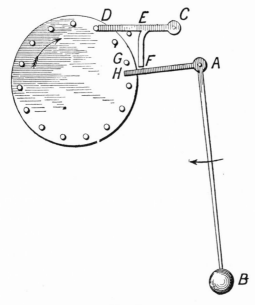

FIG. 40.

arm *A H* was lowered, the ratchet had got into
position again and its point *D* was ready to meet
and stop the next pin that was coming on against
it. At each blow of the pins against the pendulum
a "tick" is made, at each blow of a pin against
the ratchet a "tock" is sounded, so that as it

moves the pendulum makes the "tick-tock" sound with which we are all familiar.

Hence then a clock consists of a wheel, or train of wheels, urged by a weight or spring, which strives continually to spin round, but its rotation is controlled by an escapement and pendulum, so contrived as only to allow it to go a step forward at regular equal intervals of time.

But this would make only a poor sort of escapement. For the mode of driving the pendulum adds a complication to the swing of the pendulum. Instead of the pendulum being simply under the accelerative force of gravity, it is also subjected to the acceleration of the pin G. This acceleration is not of the "harmonic" order. Hence so far as it goes it does not tend to assist in giving a harmonic motion to the pendulum, but, on the contrary, disturbs that harmonic motion. Besides this, the impulse of the pin is in practice not always uniform. For if the wheel is at the end of a train of wheels driven by a weight, though the force acting on it is constant, yet, as that force is transmitted through a train of wheels, it is much affected by the friction of the oil. And on colder days the oil becomes more coagulated, and offers greater resistance. Moreover, as will be explained more in detail afterwards, the fact that the impulse is administered by G at the end of the stroke of the pendulum is disadvantageous, as it interferes with the free play of the pendulum.

From all these causes the above escapement is imperfect in character, and would not do where precision was required.

It is now time to return to the old-fashioned escapements which were in use before the time of Galileo. These consisted of a wheel called a crown wheel, with triangular teeth. On one side of this wheel a vertical axis was fitted, with projecting "pallets" *e f*. Across the axis a verge or rod *e f* was placed, fitted with a ball at each end. When the crown wheel attempted to move on, one of its teeth came in contact with a pallet. This urged the pallet forward, and thereby caused an impulse to be given to the axis, on which was mounted the

FIG. 41.

verge, carrying the balls. These of course began to move under the acceleration of the force thus impressed upon the pallet. Meantime, however, the other pallet was moving in the opposite direction, and by the time the first pallet had been pushed so far that it escaped or slid past the tooth of the crown wheel, which was pressing upon it, the other pallet had come into contact with the tooth on the other side of the crown wheel. This tended to arrest the motion of the verge, to bring

the balls to a standstill, and ultimately to impart a
motion in a contrary direction to them.

Thus then the arrangement was that of a
pendulum not acted on by gravity, for the balls
neutralised one another. The pendulum was,
however, not subjected to a harmonic acceleration,
but alternately to a nearly uniform acceleration
from A to B and B to A. As a result, therefore,
the time of oscillation was
not independent of the arc
of swing, but varied according to it, as also according
to the driving power of the
crown wheel. At each stroke
there was a considerable
"recoil." For as each tooth
of the wheel came into play
it was unable at first to
overcome and drive back the
pallet against which it was

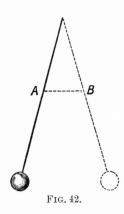

FIG. 42.

pressing, but, on the contrary, was for a time itself
driven back by the pallet.

Of course, so long as the motions of the wheel
and verge were exactly uniform, fair time was kept.
But the least inequality of manufacture produced
differences.

Nevertheless it was on this principle that clocks
were made during the thirteenth, fourteenth and
fifteenth centuries. They were mostly made for

cathedrals and monasteries. One was put up at Westminster, erected out of money paid as a fine upon one of the few English judges who have been convicted of taking bribes.

The time of swing of these clocks depended entirely upon the ratio of the mass of the balls at the end of the verge as compared with the strength of the driving force by which the acceleration on the pallets was produced. They were very commonly driven by a spring instead of a weight. The spring consisted of a long strip of rather poor quality steel coiled up on a drum. As it unwound it became weaker, and thus the acceleration on the verge became weaker, and the clock went slower.

In order, therefore, to keep the time true, it became necessary to devise some arrangement by which the driving force on the crown wheel should be kept more constant.

This gave rise to the invention of the fusee. The spring was put inside a drum or cylindrical box. One end of the spring was fastened to an axis, which was kept fixed while the clock was going; the other was fastened to the inside of the drum. Round the drum a cord was wound, which, as the drum was moved by the spring, tended to be wound up on the surface of the drum. Owing to the unequal pull of the spring, this cord was pulled by the drum strongly at first, and afterwards more feebly. To compensate its action a conical wheel was provided, with a spiral path cut in it in such a way and of such a size and proportion that as the wheel was turned round by the pull of the drum the cord was on different parts of it, so that the leverage or turning power on it varied, becoming greater as the pull of the cord became weaker, and in such a ratio that one just compen-

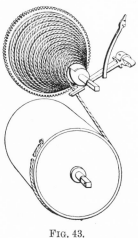

sated the other, and the turning power of the axle was kept uniform.

In this manner small table clocks were made which kept very toler-able time.

Huygens converted these clocks into pen-dulum clocks in a very simple manner. He re-moved one of the balls, lengthened the verge, and slightly increased the weight of the other

FIG. 43.

ball. By this means, while the crown wheel still continued to drive the verge and remaining ball, the acceleration on that ball now no longer depended entirely on the force of the crown wheel. The acceleration and retardation were now almost en-tirely governed by the force of gravity on the remaining ball, and this acceleration was harmonic.

The clock, therefore, was immensely improved as a time-keeper. Still, however, the acceleration remained partly due to the driving power, and this was partly non-harmonic and introduced errors.

Most of the old clocks were converted shortly after the time of Huygens. As there was in general no room for the pendulum inside the clock-case, they usually brought the axle on which the pallets were mounted outside the clock and made it vibrate in front of the face.

Many old clocks exist, of which the engraving in the frontispiece is an example, that have been thus converted. A true old verge escapement clock is now a rarity.

The type of escapement invented by Galileo never came into vogue for clocks, on account of its imperfections, except till after a long interval, when, with certain modifications, it became the basis of a new improvement at the hands of Sir George Airey.

The crown wheel fell into disuse and was replaced by the anchor escapement, which was employed in that popular and excellent timepiece used throughout the eighteenth and the early part of the nineteenth century, and is now known as "The Grandfather's Clock." It was after all the crown wheel in another shape. The wheel, however, was flattened out, the teeth being put in the same plane. This made it much easier to construct. The pallets were fixed on an axis, and were a little altered so

as to suit the changed arrangement of the teeth.
The pendulum was no longer hung on the axis
which carried the pallets. A cause of a good deal
of friction and loss of power was thus removed.
The pendulum was hung from a strip of thin steel
spring, which allowed it to oscillate, and which
supported it without friction.   This excellent
manner of suspending pendulums is now universal.

FIG. 44.

It enabled the pendulum to be made very heavy.
The bob was usually some eight or nine pounds
weight.   By this means the acceleration on the
pendulum was due almost entirely to gravity acting
on the bob, and thus the motion of the pendulum
became almost wholly harmonic.   Whence it followed that variations in the pendulum swing
became of secondary importance, and did not
greatly alter the going of the clock.

Therefore when the wheels became worn, and the pivots choked with old oil and dust, the old clock still went on. If it showed a tendency to stop for want of power, a little more was added to the driving weight, and the clock kept as good time as ever.

The swing of the pendulum was by this escapement enabled to be made small, so that the arc of swing of the bob differed but little from a cycloid.

The secret of the time-keeping qualities of these old " Grandfather" clocks is the length of pendulum. This renders it possible to have but a small arc of oscillation, and therefore the motion is kept very nearly harmonic. For practical purposes nothing will even now beat these old clocks, of which one should be in every house. At present the tendency is to abolish them and to substitute American clocks with very short pendulums, which never can keep good time. They are made of stamped metal. When they get out of order no one thinks of having them mended. They are thrown into the ash-pit and a new one bought. In reality this is not economy.

Good " Grandfather " clocks are not now often made. The last place I remember to have seen them being manufactured is at Morez, in the district of the Jura. An excellent clock, enclosed in a dust-tight iron case, with a tall painted case of quaint old design, can be bought for about 55s. The wheels are well cut, and the internal mechanism very good.

I visited the town of Morez in the year 1893. The clock industry was declining. The farmers of France seemed to prefer small clocks of hideous appearance, made in Germany and in America, to the excellent work of their own country. Probably by now the old clockmaking industry is extinct. One I purchased at that time has gone well ever since.

CHAPTER IV.

It is now time to give a description of the various parts of an ordinary pendulum clock. We will take the " Grandfather " clock as an example. We shall want an hour hand and a minute hand in the centre of the face, and a seconds hand to show seconds a little above them. There will be a seconds pendulum 39·14 inches long, and the centre of the face of the clock will be about seven feet above the ground, so as to give practically about five feet of fall for the weight.

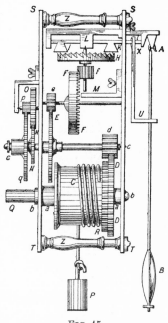

FIG. 45.

In the first place, we have to consider the axle which carries the minute hand, and which turns round once in each hour. This is usually made of a piece of steel about one-sixth of an inch in diameter. Clockmakers usually call an axle an " arbor," or " tree," whence our word axletree.

This " arbor " is turned in the lathe, so as to have pivots on each end, fitted into holes in the clock plates, that is to say, the flat pieces of brass that serve as the body of the clock. The adjoining diagram shows $S\,T$ the clock faces, and C, the arbor of the minute hand.

Inasmuch as the seconds hand is to turn round

sixty times while the minute hand turns round once, it is obvious that the arbor of the

FIG. 46.

minute hand must be connected to the arbor of the seconds hand by a train of cogwheels so arranged as to multiply by sixty. This of course involves us in having large and small cogwheels.

The small cogwheels usually have eight teeth, and are for convenience of manufacture, as also to stand prolonged wear, cut out of the solid steel of the arbor. They are nicely polished.

The easiest pair of wheels to use will be two pinions of eight teeth, or "leaves," as they are called, and two cogwheels, one of sixty-four teeth, the other of sixty teeth.

It is then clear that if the arbor A turns round

once in an hour, t̶   ̶ʳbor *B* will turn round
eight times in aⁿ   nd *C* will turn round
$\dfrac{60 \times 64}{8 \times 8} = 60$ tiᵢ   ̶ʳ, or once in each
minute.

By having 480 teeth ̶   ̶ᵉl on *A*, you

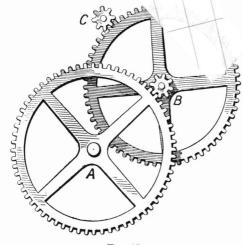

FIG. 47.

could, of course, make *C* go round once in a minute
without the use of any intermediate arbor such as *B*.

But this would not be a very convenient plan.
For as the wheel on *A* is usually about two and
a quarter inches in diameter, to cut 480 teeth
on so small a wheel would involve us in cutting
about sixty teeth to the inch. The teeth would

thus be microscopically small, and would have to
be set so fine that the least dirt would clog them.
Moreover, the pinion of eight leaves would have to
be microscopic. For these reasons, therefore, it is
usual in clocks not to use wheels with teeth more
than sixty or sixty-four in number, and to diminish
the motion gradually by means, where needful, of
intermediate arbors. We have next to
consider how the weight is to be arranged
so as to turn the arbor A once round in
an hour. We know that we have five feet
of space for the weights to fall in. If we
arrange to have what is called a double
fall, as shown in the sketch, then, allowing
room for pulley wheels, we shall find that
our string may be practically about nine
feet in length.

FIG. 48.

The clock will be wanted to go for a
week without winding, and as people may
forget to wind it at the proper hour of the day, we
will give it a day extra, and make an " eight-day "
clock of it. Hence then, while nine feet of cord is
being pulled out by a weight which falls four and
a half feet, the minute hand is to be turned round
as many times as there are hours in eight days,
viz., 192 times. This could be accomplished, of
course, by winding the cord round the arbor of the
minute hand. But this would require 192 turns.
If our cord is to be ordinary whipcord, or catgut,

say one-twelfth of an inch in diameter, in order
that the cord could be wound upon it, the arbor
would have to be $\frac{192}{12}$ inches long $= 14\frac{1}{3}$ inches
long. This would make the clock case unnecessarily
deep. We must
therefore again
have recourse to an
intermediate wheel.

If we put a pinion
of eight leaves on
the minute hand
arbor c, and engage
it with a wheel of
sixty-four teeth on
another arbor b,
then b will ob-
viously turn round
once in eight hours,
that is to say,
twenty-four times
in the period of
eight days. And, if
we fix on b a

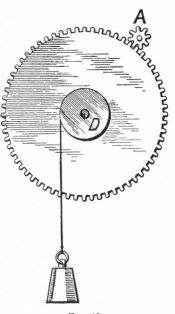

FIG. 49.

"drum" or cylinder two inches long, the twenty-
four turns of our cord will just fit upon it, since,
as has been said, our cord is to be one-twelfth of
an inch in diameter. The diameter of the drum
must be such that a cord nine feet long can be

wound twenty-four times round it. That is to say, each lap must take $\dfrac{9 \times 12}{24} = 4\frac{1}{2}$ inches of cord. From this it is easy to calculate that the diameter of the drum must be rather less than one and a half inches. From this then it results that we want for a "Grandfather's" clock a drum two inches long and one and a half inches diameter, on this a cogwheel of sixty-four teeth working into a minute hand arbor, with a pinion-wheel with eight leaves, and a cogwheel of sixty-four teeth, an intermediate or idle wheel with an eight-leaved pinion, and a cogwheel of sixty teeth, engaging with a seconds hand arbor with a pinion of eight leaves. This is called the "train of wheels." With it a weight such as can be arranged in an ordinary "Grandfather's" clock case will cause by its fall during eight days the second hand arbor to turn round once in each minute during the whole time, and the minute hand arbor to turn round once in each hour.

We must next provide an arrangement for winding the clock up. It is obvious that we cannot do so by twisting the hands back. It is true that this could be done, but it would take about five minutes to do each time and be wearisome. In order to save this trouble, an arrangement called a ratchet wheel and pall must be provided. A ratchet wheel consists of a wheel with a series of notches cut in

it, as shown in the figure A. A pall is a piece of
metal, mounted on a pin, and kept pressed up
against the ratchet wheel by a spring C. It is
obvious that if I turn the wheel A round, and
thus wind up a weight, fastened to a cord wound
round the drum D, that
the pall B will go click-
click-click as the ratchet
wheel goes round, but
that the pall will hold it
from slipping back again.
When, however, I take
my hands away, and let
the ratchet wheel alone,
then the weight E will
pull on the drum D, and
try and turn the ratchet
wheel back the opposite
way to that in which I
twisted it at first. If
the pall B is held fast,
it is impossible to move
it, but if the pall is fixed

FIG. 50.

to a cogwheel F, which rides loose on the arbor
of the drum D, then the pull of the weight E
will tend to twist the cogwheel F round, and this,
if engaged with a pinion wheel on the minute
hand arbor, will therefore drive the clock. As
the clock arbors move, of course the weight E

gradually runs down, and, at last all the string is unwound from the drum D. The clock is said then to have "run down," but if I take a clock key, and by means of it wind the string up upon the drum D, then the pall lets the drum and

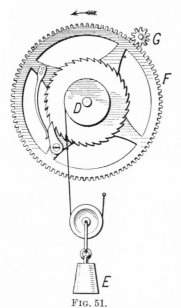

ratchet slip; the clock hands are not affected. When I have given twenty-four turns to the arbor, the nine feet of cord will then be wound upon the drum again, and the clock will be ready to go for eight more days, and will begin to move as soon as I cease to press upon the clock key.

FIG. 51.

I have thus described the winding mechanism. It now remains to describe the escapement.

It is of course obvious that, if the weight and train of wheels were simply let go, the weight would rush down, and the seconds-hand wheel would fly round at a tremendous pace; but we want it to be so restrained as only to be allowed to go one-sixtieth part of its journey round in each second. In fact, we need an "escapement" and a pendulum.

The escapement usually employed in "Grand-father" clocks is the anchor escapement above described. It is not by any means the best sort of escapement, but it is the easiest to make; and hence its popularity in the days sometimes called the "dear, good old days," when people had to file everything out by hand, and had to take a day to do badly what can now be done well in five minutes.

The escape wheel of an anchor escapement has thirty sharp angular teeth on its rim. The wheel is made as light as possible, so that the shock of stoppage at each tick of the clock may be as slight as possible, for a heavy blow of course wastes power and gradually wears out the clock. The anchor consists of two arms of the shape shown in the illustration (Fig. 44). As the escape wheel goes round in the direction of the arrow, the anchor, mounted on its arbor, rocks to and fro. The wheel cannot run away, because the act of pushing one arm or "pallet," as it is called, outwards, and thus freeing the tooth pulls the other pallet in, and this stops the motion of the tooth opposite to it, but when the anchor rocks back again, so as to disengage the pallet from the tooth that holds it, then the opposite tooth is free to fly forward against the

K 2

other pallet. This tends to rock the anchor the other way, but at that instant the pallet just engages the next tooth of the wheel, and so the action goes on. The anchor rocks from side to side ; the pallets alternately engage the teeth of the wheel, making at each rock of the anchor the tick-tock sound with which we are so familiar. If the anchor were free to rock at any speed it could, the ticking of the clock would be very quick; so, to restrain the vivacity of the anchor, we have a pendulum. The pendulum might be simply hung on to the anchor. But the disadvantage of doing this would be that the heavy bob of the pendulum would cause such a pressure on the arbor of the anchor that there would be great friction, and the arbor would soon be worn out, and the accurate going of the clock disturbed. The pendulum therefore is hung on a piece of steel spring on a separate hook, which lets it go backwards and forwards and carries the weight easily, while a rod projecting from the anchor has a pin, which works in a slot on the pendulum. The pendulum is therefore able to control and regulate the movements of the escapement, and thus the time of the clock.

Of course it is clear that the heavier the driving weight put on the drum of the clock, and the better the cut and finish of the wheels, and the greater the cleanliness and oil, the more will be the pressure tending to drive round the escape wheel, and the harder the pressure on the pallets, and hence the bigger the impulses on the pendulum, and therefore the larger the amplitude of its swing.

If the amplitude of the pendulum's swing affected the time of its swing, then the time kept by the clock would vary with the weight, and the dirt and friction, and the drying up of the oil. But here precisely is where the value of the beautiful law governing the harmonic motion of the pendulum comes in. The time of the pendulum is (for small arcs) independent of the length of swing, and therefore of the driving force of the clock, and hence within limits the clock, even though roughly made and foul with the dirt of years, continues to keep good time. But the anchor escapement has imperfections. The only way in which a pendulum can be relied on to keep accurate time is by leaving it unimpeded. But the pressure of the teeth on the pallets in an anchor escapement constantly interferes with this.

A little consideration will easily show that there are some times during the swing of a pendulum at which interference is far more fatal to its time-keeping than at others. Thus the bob of a pendulum may be regarded as a weight shot outwards from its position of rest against the influence of a retarding force varying as its distance from rest—in fact, shot out against a spring. The

time of going out and coming in again will be quite
independent of the force exerted to throw it out,
quite independent of its original velocity. Therefore a variation in the impulse given to the bob is
of no consequence, provided that impulse is given
when the bob is near the position of rest. This
follows from the nature of the motion. If a ball
be attached to a piece of elastic thread, and thrown
from the hand, so that it flies out, and then stops
and is brought back by the elastic force of the
thread, the time of the outward motion and the
return is the same whatever be the force of
the throw. And so if a pendulum be impelled
outwards from a position of rest, the time of the
swing out and back is the same, however big (within
limits) is the impelling force and the consequent
length of the swing. The use of a pendulum as
a measure of time is to impel it outwards, and then
let it fly *freely* out and back. But if its motion is
not free, if forces other than gravity act upon it
while on its path, then its time of swing will be
disturbed. It does not matter with what force you
originally impel it, but what does matter is, that
when it once starts it should be allowed to travel
unimpeded and uninfluenced. Now that is what
an anchor escapement does not do. The impulse
is given the whole way out on one of the pallets,
and then when it is at its extreme of swing, and
ought to be left tranquil, the other pallet fastens

on it. But a perfect escapement ought to give its
impulse at the middle point of the swing, when the
pendulum is at the lowest, and then cease, and
allow the pendulum to adapt its swing to the
impulse it has received, and
thus therefore to keep its time
constant. This is done by an
escapement called the dead
beat escapement, which,
though in an imperfect way,
realises these conditions.

FIG. 52.

The alteration is made in
the shape of the pallets of
the anchor. The wheel is much the same. Each
pallet consists of two faces: a driving face $a\,b$
and a sliding face $b\,c$.

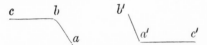

When the tooth b has done its work by pressing on the driving face, and thus driving the
anchor over, say, to the left, then the tooth on
the opposite side falls on the sliding face of the
other pallet. This being an arc of a circle, has
no effect in driving the anchor one way or the
other; hence the pendulum is free to swing to
the left as far as it likes and return when it feels
inclined, always with the exception of a little
friction of the tooth on the faces of the pallets,

but when it returns and begins to move towards the right, the tooth slides back along the face of the pallet till the pendulum is almost at the middle of its swing; then an impulse is given by the pressure of the tooth upon the inclined plane a' b'. As soon, however, as the tooth leaves b', another tooth on the other side at once engages the sliding face b c of the other pallet, and so the motion goes on.

This beautiful escapement is at present used for astronomical clocks; the pallets are made of agate or sapphire, and therefore do not grind away the teeth of the wheel perceptibly, and the loss by friction on the sliding surfaces is exceedingly small.

There are several other ways even better than this for securing a free pendulum movement. We have now to return to our clock.

The centre arbor moves round once in an hour, and carries the minute hand. In order to provide an hour hand, which shall turn round once in twelve hours, we fasten a cogwheel and tube N on to the minute hand arbor by means of a small spring, which keeps it rather tight, but allows it to slip if turned round hard (see Fig. 45). This spring is a little bent plate slipped in behind the cogwheel on which its ends rest; its centre presses on a shoulder on the minute hand arbor; it is a sort of small carriage spring. The cogwheel n has thirty teeth.

This cogwheel engages another cogwheel *o* with thirty teeth, on a separate arbor, which carries a third cogwheel, *p*, with six teeth, and this again engages a fourth cogwheel, *q*, with seventy-two teeth, mounted on a tube which slips over the tube to which the cogwheel *a* is attached. It is now easy to see that for each turn of the minute hand arbor the arbor *p* makes one turn, and for each turn of the arbor *p* the cogwheel *d*, makes one-twelfth of a turn. From which it follows that for each turn of the minute hand arbor the cogwheel *d* with its tube, or, as it is sometimes called, its "slieve," makes one-twelfth of a turn, and thus makes a hand fastened to it show one hour for every complete turn of the minute hand.

The minute hand is attached to the tube or slieve which carries the cogwheel *N*. The hour hand is attached to the tube or slieve which carries the cogwheel *Q*, and one goes twelve times as slowly as the other.

But if you want to set the clock it is easy to do so by reason of the fact that the minute hand is not fixed to the arbor, but only to the slieve on the cogwheel that fits on the arbor, and is held somewhat tight to the arbor by means of the spring. The hands can thus be turned, but they are a little stiff. A washer on the minute hand arbor keeps the slieve on the cogwheel pressed tight against the spring, being secured in its turn by a very small lynch-pin driven through a hole in the minute hand arbor.

It remains to explain a few subsidiary arrangements, not always found upon all clocks, but which are useful.

In order to prevent the overwinding of the clock (see Fig. 43), which would cause the cord to overrun the drum, an arm is provided, fitted with a spring. As the weight is wound up the free part of the cord travels along the drum or the fusee; and the cord, when it is near the end of the winding, comes up against the arm and pushes it a little aside. This causes the end of the arm to be pushed against a stop on the axis of the fusee, and thus prevents the clock being further wound up. The stop, being ratchet-shaped, does not prevent the weight from pulling the ratchet wheel round the other way, and thus driving the clock; it only prevents the rotation of that wheel when the string is near it, and the winding is finished.

Another arrangement is the "maintaining spring."

It will be remembered that during the process of winding the clock the hand twisting the key takes the pressure of the ratchet wheel off the pall, so that during that operation no force is at work to drive the clock. In consequence the pendulum receives no impulse, but swings simply by virtue of its former motion. If the process of winding were

done slowly enough the clock might even stop.   To
avoid this, a very ingenious arrangement is made to
keep the cogwheel mounted on the winding shaft
going during the winding-up process. This is called
a maintaining spring.

The arrangement shown in Fig. 53 will explain it.

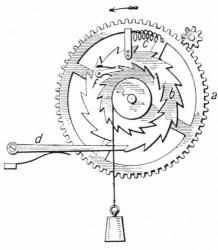

FIG. 53.

The cogwheel *a* and the ratchet wheel are both
mounted loosely on the arbor carrying the drum.
a is linked to *b* by a spring *c*. The ratchet wheel
b is engaged by a pall fixed to some convenient place
on the body of the clock frame. When the weight
pulls on the drum the pull is communicated to the
ratchet wheel *b*, and this acts on the spring *c* and

pulls it out a little. As soon as the spring *c* is pulled out as far as its elasticity permits, a pull is communicated to the cogwheel *a*, and the clock is driven round. When the clock is wound the pressure of the weight is removed, and therefore the ratchet wheel *e* no longer presses on the pall, and thus no pressure is communicated to the ratchet wheel *b*, or through it to the clock. But here the spring *c* comes into play. For since the ratchet wheel *b* is held fast by the pall *d*, the spring *c* pulls at the wheel *a*, and thus for a minute or so will continue to drive the clock. This driving force, it is true, is less than that caused by the weight, but it is just enough to keep the pendulum going for a short time, so that the going of the clock is not interfered with.

If the reader can get possession of a clock, preferably one that does not strike, and, with the aid of a small pair of pincers and one or two screwdrivers, will take it to pieces and put it together again, the mechanism above described will soon become familiar to him. Not every clock is provided with maintaining spring and overwinding preventer.

The cause of stoppage of a clock generally is dirt. Where possible, clocks should always be put under glass cases. "Grandfather" clocks will go much better if brown paper covers are fitted over the works under the cases. In this way a quantity of dust may be avoided. To get a good oil is very important.

It will be noticed that pivot-holes in clocks are usually provided with little cup-like depressions. This is to aid in keeping in the oil. The best clock oil is that which does not easily solidify or evaporate. Ordinary machine oil, such as used for sewing machines, is good as a lubricant, but rapidly evaporates. Olive oil corrodes the brass.

It is best to procure a little clock oil, or else the oil used for gun locks, sold by the gunsmiths. The holes should be cleaned out with the end of a wooden lucifer match, cut to a tapering point. The pivots should be well rubbed with a rag dipped in spirits of wine. If the pivots are worn they should be repolished in the lathe. If the cogs of the wheels are worn, there is no remedy but to get new ones. Old clocks sometimes want a little addition to the driving weight to make them go.

The weight necessary to drive the clock depends on its goodness of construction, and on the weight of the pendulum. If the clock is driven for eight days with a cord of nine feet in length with a double fall, then during each beat of the pendulum that weight will descend by an amount $=$

$$\frac{9}{2 \times 24 \times 60 \times 60 \times 8} \text{ feet or } \tfrac{1}{12800}\text{th inch.}$$

Whence, if the clock weight is 10 lbs., the impulse received by the clock at each beat is equivalent to a weight of 10 lbs. falling through $\tfrac{1}{12880}$th of an inch, or to the fall of six grains through an inch.

The power thus expended goes in friction of the wheels and hands, and in maintaining the pendulum in spite of the friction of the air.

The work therefore that is put into the clock by the operation of winding is gradually expended during the week in movement against friction. The work is indestructible. The friction of the parts of the clock develops heat, which is dissipated over the room and gradually absorbed in nature. But this heat is only another form of work. Amounts of work are estimated in pressures acting through distances. Thus, if I draw up a weight of 1 lb. against the accelerative force of gravity through a distance of one foot, I am said to do a foot-pound of work.

One pound of coal consumed in a perfect engine would do eight millions foot-pounds of work. Hence, if the energy in a pound of coal could be utilized, it would keep about 100,000 grandfather's clocks going for a week. As it is consumed in an ordinary steam engine it will do about half a million foot-pounds of work. One pound of bread contains about three million foot-pounds of energy. A man can eat about three pounds of bread in a day, and, as he is a very good engine, he can turn this into about three-quarters of a million foot-pounds of work. The rest of the work contained in the bread goes off in the form of heat.

As has been previously said, the power of the

action of gravity in drawing back a pendulum that has been pushed aside from its position of rest becomes less in proportion as the pendulum is longer, and hence as the pendulum is longer the time of vibrations increases. In the appendix to this chapter a short proof will be given showing that the length of a pendulum varies as the square of the time of its vibration. A pendulum which is 39·14 inches in length vibrates at London once in each second. Of course at other parts of the earth, where the force of gravity is slightly different, the time of vibration will be different, but, since the earth is nearly a globe in

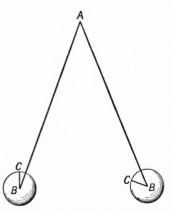

FIG. 54.

shape, the force of gravity at different parts of it does not vary much, and therefore the time of vibration of the same pendulum in different parts of the earth does not vary very much. The length of a pendulum is measured from its point of suspension down to a point in the bob or weight. At first sight one would be inclined to think that the centre of gravity of the pendulum would be the point to which you must measure in order to get its length. So that if *B* were a circular bob, and the rod of the pendulum were very light, the distance *A B* to the centre of the bob would be the length of the pendulum. But if we were to fly to this conclusion, we should be making the same error that Galileo made when he allowed a ball to *roll* down an inclined plane.

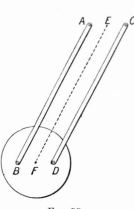

FIG. 55.

He forgot that the motion was not a simple one of a body down a plane, but was also a rolling motion. The pendulum does not vibrate so as always to keep the bob immovable with the top side *C* always uppermost. On the contrary, at each beat the bob rotates on its centre and makes, as it were, some swings of its own. Therefore in the total motions of the pendulum this rotation of the bob has to be taken into account. Of course, if the pendulum were so arranged that the bob did not rotate, and the point *C* were always uppermost, as, for instance, if the pendulum consisted of two parallel rods, *A B* and *C D*, suspended from *A* and *C*, then we might consider the bob as that of a pendulum suspended from *E*, and the pendulum would swing once in a second if $AB = CD = EF$ were equal to 39·14 inches, for by this arrangement there would be no rotation of the bob. But as pendulums are generally made with the bob rigidly fixed to the rod $E\,F$, the rotation must be taken into account.

It wants some rather advanced mathematical knowledge to do this. But in practice clockmakers take no account of it. The correction is not a large one, so they make the rod as nearly true as they can, arrange a screw on the bob to allow of adjustment, and then screw the bob up and down until in practice the time of oscillation is found to be correct.

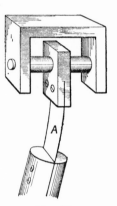

FIG. 56.

The mode of suspension of a pendulum of the best class is that shown in Fig. 56, which allows the pendulum to fall into its true position without strain. A is a tempered steel spring, which bends to and fro at each oscillation. It is wonderful how long these springs can be bent to and fro without breaking. Inasmuch as lengthening the pendulum increases the time, so that the time of vibration t varies as the square of the length of the pendulum, a very small lengthening of the pendulum causes a difference in the time. In practice, for each thousandth of an inch that we lengthen the pendulum we make a difference of about one second a day in the going of the clock. If we cut a screw with eighteen threads to the inch on the bottom of the pendulum rod, and put a circular nut on it, with the rim divided into sixty parts, then each turn through one division will raise or lower the bob by $\frac{1}{1080}$th of an inch, and this first causes an alteration of time of the clock by one second in the day. This is a convenient arrangement in practice, for it affords an easy

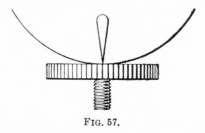

FIG. 57.

means of adjusting the pendulum. We need only observe how many seconds the clock loses or gains in the day, and then turn the nut through a corresponding number of divisions in order to rectify the pendulum.

Another needful correction of the pendulum is that due to changes in temperature. If the rod of the pendulum be made of thoroughly dried mahogany, soaked in a weak solution of shellac in spirits of wine, and then dried, there will not be much variation either from heat or moisture.

But for clocks required to have great precision the pendulum rod is usually made of metal. A rod of iron expands about $\frac{1}{160000}$th of its length for each degree Fahrenheit; and therefore for each degree Fahrenheit a pendulum rod of 39·14 inches will expand about $\frac{1}{4000}$ thousandths of an inch, and thus make a difference in the going of the clock of about one-fourth of a second per day. The expansion will, of course, make the clock go slower. It would be possible to correct this expansion if some arrangement could be made, whenever it occurred, to lift up the bob of the pendulum by an

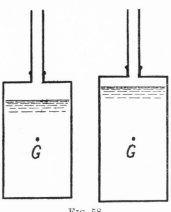

FIG. 58.

amount corresponding to it, as, for instance, to make the bob of some material which expanded very much more by heat than the material of which the pendulum rod was made.

Thus if we hang on to the end of a pendulum of iron a bottle of iron about seven inches long, and almost fill it with mercury, then, as soon as the heat increases, the iron of the rod and of the bottle expands, and the centre of oscillation of the

L 2

pendulum is lowered. But as the linear expansion
of mercury contained in a bottle is about five times
that of iron, the mercury rises in the bottle, and thus
the expansion downwards of the pendulum rod is
compensated by the expansion upwards of the
mercury in the bottle. The rod may be fastened to
the mouth of the bottle by a screw, so that as the
bottle is turned round it may be raised or lowered
on the rod, and thus the length of the pendulum
may be adjusted. The bottle is made of steel tube,
screwed into a thin turned iron top and bottom. Of
course no solder must be used to unite the iron, for
mercury dissolves solder. A little oil and white-lead
will make the screwed joints tight. This is an
excellent form of pendulum. Another plan is to
use zinc as the metal which is to counteract the
expansion of the iron. The expansion of zinc is
about three times that of iron.

Hence a zinc tube, about twenty inches long
(shown shaded in Fig. 59), is made to rest upon
a disc fastened to the lower part of the iron
pendulum rod. On the top of the zinc rests a
flat ring A, from which is suspended an iron
tube A, which carries the bob B. The expansion of the zinc tube is large enough to compensate
the expansion both of the rod and the tube, and
the bob consequently remains at the same depth
below the point of suspension, whatever be the
temperature.

There is, however, a new method which is far
superior to all these, and this is due to the discovery by M. Guilliaume, of Paris, of a compound
of nickel and steel which expands so little that it
can be compensated by a bob of lead
instead of by a bob of mercury. This
material is sold in England under the
name of " invar." An invar rod with a
properly proportioned lead bob makes
an almost perfect pendulum, the expansion of the invar and the lead going
on together. The exact expansion of
the invar is given by the makers, who
also supply information as to the size
and suspension of the bob proper to
use with it.

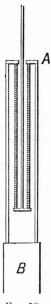

FIG. 59.

It has been already shown that the
uniformity of time of swing of a pendulum is only true when the arc
through which it swings is very small.
If the total swing from one side to
another is not more than about two
inches very little difference in time-
keeping is made by putting a little more driving
weight on the clock, and thus increasing its arc
of swing; but when the arc of swing becomes say
three inches, or one and a half inches on each
side of the pendulum, then the time of vibration
is affected. At this distance each tenth of an inch

increase of swing makes the pendulum go slower by about a second a day.

The resistance of the air, of course, has a great influence on a pendulum, and is one of the chief causes that bring it ultimately to rest. Even the variations of pressure of the atmosphere which the barometer shows as the weather varies have an effect on the going of a clock. Attempts have been made by fixing barometers on to pendulums with an ingenious system of counter balancing to counteract this, but these refinements are not in common use, and are too complicated to be susceptible of effective regulation.

APPENDIX TO CHAPTER IV.

It may be useful to give a simple form of proof of the law which governs the time of oscillation of a pendulum whose length is given.

Unfortunately, it is impossible to give one so simple as to be comprehended by those who know nothing whatever of mathematics. It is, however, possible to give a proof that requires very little mathematical knowledge.

We know that when a mass of matter is whirled round at the end of a string it tends to fly outwards and puts a strain on the string. The faster the speed at which the mass is whirled, the stronger will be the strain on the string. Suppose that the length of the string equals R, the velocity of the mass as it flies round equals V. Let *a* be the body whirled round by a string *o a* from a centre at *O*. The body always, of course, tends to fly on in a straight line from the point at which it is at any instant. But that tendency is frustrated by the pull of the string which constrains it to take a circular path. It is, of course, all one whether the force that tends to pull the body inwards towards *O* is a string or an attractive force of any kind acting through a distance without any string at all. Evidently if the body keeps its place in the circle it must be because the centrifugal force tending to whirl it out is equal to the centripetal or attractive force tending to pull it in.

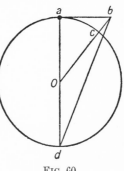

FIG. 60.

The strain on the body, due to the force tending to pull it inwards, we shall designate by F, meaning by F the number of feet of velocity that would in one second be imparted to the body by the attractive force.

Suppose that at some given instant of time the body is at a point *a*. At that instant its *direction* will be along *a b*, tangential to the circle at *a*, and that is the path it would take if the centripetal or attractive force ceased to act just as the body got to *a*. In that case the body would be whirled off like a stone from a sling along the line $a\,b$, and would at the end of a given time, let us suppose a second, arrive at b. But it is not so whirled off; it is attracted towards O and pulled inwards, and comes to c. Hence, then, the attractive force acting during one second must have been sufficient to pull the mass in from b to c. But we know that if an accelerating force (F) acts on a body for a second it produces a final velocity equal to F at the end of the second, and an average velocity half F during the second.

Hence, then, the space $b\,c$, by which the body has been pulled in, is represented by half F, but $a\,b$, the space which the body would have travelled forwards, will be represented by V, the velocity of the body in a second; but if the motion be such that the distance $b\,c$ travelled in a second is very small, then the triangles $a\,b\,d$ and $a\,b\,c$ are approximately similar, and the smaller $a\,b$ is the more nearly similar they are. Whence then $\dfrac{a\,b}{b\,c} = \dfrac{a\,d}{a\,b}$, that is to say $(a\,b)^2 = a\,d \times b\,c$.

But $a\,b$ represents the space which would have been traversed by the body in one second at the rate it was going, and hence is equal to V; $a\,d$ is the diameter of the circle, and hence equals 2 R; $b\,c$ is the space through which the body has been drawn in the second by the attractive force F, and therefore equals half F.

Whence then $V^2 = 2\,R \times$ half $F = R\,F$.

We took a second as the limit of time during which the motion was to be considered. Of course any other time could have been taken. Now what is true of the motion of a body during a very short time is also true of the body during the whole of its path, assuming that the path is a circle, and that F remains constant, as it obviously will if the path is a circle, and the velocity is uniform. Whence then we may generally say that if a body is being whirled round at the end of a string the strain F on the string is directly proportional to the square of the velocity, and is inversely proportional to the length of the string.

The time of rotation, is of course = length of the path ÷ velocity

$$= \frac{2\,\pi\,\mathrm{R}}{\mathrm{V}} = \frac{2\,\pi\,\mathrm{R}}{\sqrt{\mathrm{R}\,\mathrm{F}}} = 2\,\pi\sqrt{\frac{\mathrm{R}}{\mathrm{F}}}.$$

Whence then we see that for motion in a circle of a mass under the attraction of a centripetal force, or pull of a string, the time of rotation will be uniform, provided that the centripetal force always varies as the radius of the path. From this it is evident that a body fixed on to an elastic thread where the pull varies as the extension would make its rotations always in equal times. If your sling consists of elastic, whirl as you will, you can only whirl the body round so many times in a second, and no more. Any increase in your efforts only makes the string stretch, and the circle get bigger. The velocity of the body in its path of course increases, but the time it takes to go once round is invariable.

It also follows that if a body hung by a string of length l, under the action of gravity, be travelling in a circle round and round, then, *if the circle is a small one compared with the length of the string*, the inward acceleration f towards the centre will be approximately proportional to the radius r of the circle, and the time of rotation will be

$$t = 2\pi\sqrt{\frac{r}{f}}.$$

But in this case f, the inward acceleration, is to g the accleration downwards of gravity as A B : A P or

$$\frac{f}{g} = \frac{AB}{AP} = \frac{AP}{OP} = \frac{r}{l}.$$

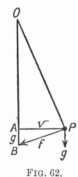

FIG. 61.   FIG. 62.

Whence then the time of rotation of this body would be if the circle of rotation was small

$$= 2\,\pi\,\sqrt{\frac{l}{g}}.$$

And if you try you will find that this is so. For
instance, take a thread $39\frac{1}{7}$ inches long, that is
3·25 feet. Hang anything heavy from one end of
it, and cause it to swing round and round in a
small circle. Now g the acceleration of gravity
= 32·2 feet per second. π the ratio of the circumference of a circle to its diameter = 3·14.
From which it follows that the time of rotation

$$= 2 \times 3\text{·}14 \sqrt{\frac{3\text{·}25}{32\text{·}2}}$$ seconds = 2 seconds. But if

we look at the rotating body sideways, it appears
to act as a pendulum; it matters nothing whether
we swing it round and round or to and fro. For
in any case the accelerative force tending to bring
it back to a position of rest is always proportional
to the distance of displacement, and, therefore, its

time of motion must always be $2\,\pi\sqrt{\frac{l}{g}}$ and its

motion harmonic.

The length of a seconds pendulum, that is a
pendulum that makes its double swing in two
seconds, will therefore be

$$l = \frac{4}{(2\,\pi)^2} \times g \text{ feet}$$

$$= \frac{g \times 12}{\pi^2} \text{ inches}$$

$$= 39\text{·}14 \text{ inches.}$$

CHAPTER V.

I HAVE thus described the principal features of ordinary clocks. For the details many treatises must be studied, and knowledge acquired which is not in any books at all.

I now, however, pass to watches. It will be remembered that a verge escapement consists of a crown wheel with teeth, engaging two pallets fixed upon a verge, furnished with balls at its extremities.

As the crown wheel was urged forwards each pallet in succession was pushed till it slipped over the tooth which was engaging it. Then a tooth on the other side came into sharp collision with the other pallet, and drove the verge the other way, and so on.

Now here we have a driving force, and a sort of pendulum. But how did the verge act as a pendulum to measure time? It is not a body rocking under the action of gravity, nor under the acceleration of a spring. How then can it act as a regulator of time, and what is the period of its swing?

The answer to this is, that it is under the

acceleration of gravity, but that gravity does not act freely on the bobs or weights, but only through the driving weight and teeth. The impulse that drives the verge is really also the accelerating force upon it, and the only accelerating force upon it.

And the worst feature about the movement is, that as the teeth and pallets move, the leverage of the teeth on the pallets alters, and thus the bobs on the verge are under the influence not of a uniform or duly regulated force, but of a constantly varying one, and one that varies in a very complicated and erratic way. It would be hopeless to expect much time-keeping from such a contrivance. The most that could be expected would be by putting on a very big weight to reduce to comparative insignificance the friction, and then hope that the swings would be uniform, so that whatever went on in one swing would go on in the next, and thus the time-keeping be regular.

But any course tending to diminish the driving force, such as the thickening of the oil, would greatly affect the going. It was for this reason that Huygens turned the verge into a pendulum by removing one of the bobs, and letting gravity thus act on the other.

For watches, however, a different plan was contrived. One end of a slender spiral spring was affixed to the verge. The other end of the spring was made fast to the clock frame. The verge was now, therefore, chiefly under the action of the acceleration of the spring. To make the acceleration of the teeth of the 'scape wheel less embarrassing, the teeth were so shaped as only to give a short push at stated intervals, and not interfere with the free swing of the verge under the alternate to-and-fro accelerations and retardations of the spring. By this means the verge became in every way an excellent pendulum, not dependent on gravity, and permitting the watch to be held in any position.

The verge thus fitted was turned into a wheel, and became a " balance wheel." It was compensated for heat expansion by a cunning use of the unequal expansion of brass and steel, in a manner analogous to the way this unequal expansion of metals had been employed to compensate the pendulum, and became the beautiful and accurate time-measurer that we see to-day, with its pivots mounted in jewels to diminish friction, and with screws round the rims of the balance wheel to enable the centre of gravity to be exactly adjusted to its centre of rotation, and with a delicate hair-spring of tempered steel that is a marvel of miscroscopic work.

But the escapement of the early watches left

much to be desired. In order to make it clear how imperfect that early escapement was, we have to turn back and remember what has been said about the dead beat escapement.

It will then be remembered that it was shown that for small arcs the pendulum would keep good time provided you let it have as much swing as it wanted to use up the force which the escapement had applied to it, *but not otherwise*, so the pendulums only acted really well when the impulse was given about the middle of the swing, and they were free to go on and stop when they pleased, and turn back at the end of it.

This essential condition was fairly approximated to in the dead beat escapement of clocks which left them at the end of their swing with only a very slight friction to impede their free motion.

But when you come to deal with a watch the case is quite different. Here the escapement is of a great size compared with the balance wheel, and the friction even of the most dead beat watch escapement that could be contrived was so big compared with the forces acting on the balance wheel as seriously to derange its motion, and render it far from a perfect time-keeper.

Now about this time—I am speaking of the

early part of the eighteenth century—a demand
of a very exceptional character arose for a really
perfect watch. The demand did not arise from
gentlemen who wanted to keep appointments to
play at ombre at their clubs, or even from mer-
chants to time their counting house hours. For
these the old-fashioned watch did very well. The
demand came from mariners. But the seamen
did not want to know the time merely to arrange
the hours for meals on the ship or to determine
when the watch was to be relieved, but for a far
more important purpose, namely, to find out by
observation of the heavens their place upon the
ocean when far out of sight of the land. It will
be very interesting to see how this problem arose,
and how the patient industry and ingenuity of man
has solved it.

The ancient navigators never went very far
from the shore, for, once out of sight of land, a
ship was out of all means of knowing where she
was. On clear days and nights the compass, and
the sun and stars would tell the mariner the
direction he was sailing in, but it was quite a
problem to determine where he was on the surface
of the earth.

Let us consider the problem. Suppose for convenience that the earth is divided up into " squares,"
as nearly, at least, as you can consider a globe to
be so marked out. Let us suppose that it has been

agreed to draw on it from pole to pole 360 lines of
longitude, commencing with one through say
Greenwich Observatory as a starting-point, and
going right round the earth till you come back to

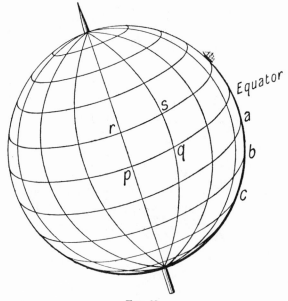

FIG. 63.

Greenwich again. Also suppose that there have
been drawn a series of circles parallel to the
equator, but going up at equal distances apart
towards the poles. Let us have 179 of these circles,
so as to leave 180 spaces, a to b, b to c, etc., from
pole to pole. This will divide the earth up like a

T.C.   M

bird-cage into squares, as if we had robed it in a
well-fitting Scotch plaid. The length measured
along the equator of the side $p\,q$ of each square at
the equator is taken as exactly sixty nautical miles
(apart from a small error of measurement, which
makes it in actual practice 59·96). This is equal
to sixty-nine and a quarter English statute miles.
The side of the square leading towards the poles $q\,s$
would also be sixty nautical miles were it not
that the earth is not truly spherical, which intro-
duces a slight error. We may, however, roughly
say that at the equator each square
measures sixty nautical miles each
way.

FIG. 64.

As we get towards the poles
the squares become rectangular
figures, with the heights of latitude
still sixty nautical miles, but the
widths becoming smaller. Thus
in England our squares measure
$p\,q = 37$ nautical miles and $q\,s = 60$ nautical
miles.

Now of course we can see at once that it is easy
at any place on the earth's surface to find your
latitude by a simple observation of the sun at noon,
if you know the day of the year, and have got a
nautical almanac. For by an instrument called a
sextant you can measure the angle he appears to
be above the horizon, and then, as you know from a

nautical almanac the angle he is above the equator,
you can soon determine your place A on the globe.
Or at night, if you measure the angular distance
that the polar star P is from the zenith, or point

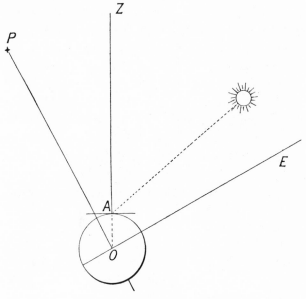

Fig. 65.

exactly over your head—that is, the angle $P\ O\ Z$—
you can subtract it from a right angle and get your
latitude, $A\ O\ E$, at once.

But how are you to determine your longitude?
The pole-star, or sun, or any other star won't help
you, for as the earth is moving they keep shifting,

and at one time or another appear exactly in the same position to everyone on the same parallel of latitude, as it is easy to see. The fact is that you are on a ball turning round. You know easily what latitude you are on, but you cannot tell your longitude unless you can tell how many hours and minutes you get to a position before Greenwich gets to the same position. If when a particular star got to Greenwich a gong were sounded which could be heard all over the earth, then of course, by seeing what stars were overhead, everyone would know their longitude at once. Perhaps by means of the new electric waves this will before long be done, and the Greenwich hours will be sounded all over the world for the use of mariners. But till this is accomplished all that can be done is to keep an accurate clock on board, so as always to give you Greenwich time.

Early attempts were made to take a pendulum clock to sea, suspending it so as to avoid disturbance to its motion by the rocking of the ship. These proved vain.

It therefore became desirable that a watch with a balance wheel should be contrived to go with a degree of accuracy in some respects comparable with the accuracy of a pendulum clock. To encourage inventors an Act of Parliament was passed in the thirteenth year of Queen Anne's reign (chapter xv.) (1713) promising a reward of

£20,000 to anyone who would invent a method of finding the longitude at sea true to half a degree— that is, true to thirty geographical miles.

If the finding of the longitude were to be accomplished by the invention of an accurate watch, then this involved the use of a watch that should not, in several months' going, have an error of more than two minutes, which is the time which the earth takes to turn through half a degree of longitude.

This was the problem which John Harrison, a carpenter, of Yorkshire, made it his life business to solve. His efforts lasted over forty years, but at the end he succeeded in winning the prize.

These instruments have been much improved by subsequent inventors, and have resulted in the construction of the modern ship's chronometer, a large watch about six inches in diameter, mounted on axles, in a mahogany box. Several of these are taken to sea by every ship.

The peculiarity of the chronometer is its escapement.

Let $A B$ be the scape wheel, and $C D$ a small lever attached to C, the pivot on which the balance wheel and spring is fastened. Let $E G$ be a lever, with a tooth F which engages the teeth of the scape wheel and prevents it moving round. Let H be a spring holding the lever $E G$ up to its work.

The lever has a spring $K E$ fastened to it at the point K. This spring is very delicate. If the lever $C D$ is turned so that the little projection M on it strikes the spring E from left to right,

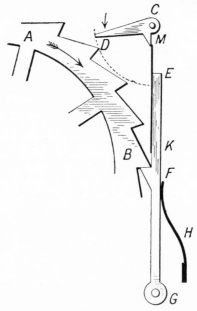

FIG. 66.

then, as the spring rests on the lever, the whole lever is pushed over, and the teeth of the scape wheel set free. At that instant, however, the escapement is so arranged that the arm $C D$ is just opposite the tooth D of the scape wheel, so that the scape wheel, instead of running away, leaps with its tooth D on to the lever $C\ D$ and swings the balance wheel round. The balance wheel is free to twist as much as it pleases, but the moment it has twisted so much that the projection M passes the spring E, then the lever $G\ E$ flies back to its place, and the scape wheel is again checked. Meanwhile the balance wheel flies round till at last it is brought to rest by the balance spring. It then recoils and sets out on its return path. This time, however, the projection M merely flips aside the spring M and the balance wheel goes back, till again it is brought to rest and returns. As soon as the lever comes opposite D the projection M then again hits the spring E, and releases the catch at F, and another tooth of the scape wheel goes by.

There then you have a completely free escapement, and consequently an accurate one. Many watches are made with these escapements, but they are more expensive than those in common use.

There is but little remaining in a watch that is not in a clock, for the wheel-trains and general arrangements are very similar.

It is possible to apply the chronometer's detached escapement to a clock. This was done by several clockmakers in the eighteenth and early part of the nineteenth century. One method of doing it is as follows :

A is a block of metal fitted to the bottom of the pendulum, B a light lever pivoted on it. C is the

scape wheel, with four teeth; D a tooth of the
scape wheel, which hops on to the projection of
the pendulum the moment that the impact of the
point E of the lever $B\ E$ has pushed aside the
lever $G\ F$, and thus released the scape wheel. The
advantage is that it is a very easy escapement to
make. But it is in reality a detached (that is to
say, a completely
free) chrono-
meter escape-
ment, as can
easily be seen.

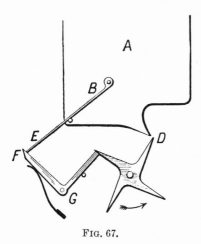

FIG. 67.

Turret - clocks
are open to con-
siderable disad-
vantages, for the
wind blowing on
the hands gives
rise to consider-
able pressure, so
that the clocks
are sometimes urging the hands against the wind,
sometimes are being helped by the wind. And this
inequality of driving force makes the pendulum at
some times make a bigger arc of swing than at others.

But we saw above that though difference of arc
of swing ought to make no difference in the time
of swing of the pendulum, yet this was only strictly
true if the arc of swing were a cycloid.

But as for practical convenience we are obliged
to make it a circle, it follows, as we saw, that for
every tenth of an inch of increase of swing of an
ordinary seconds pendulum about a second a day
of error is introduced.   To remove this difficulty a
gravity escapement was invented by Mudge in the
eighteenth century, improved by Bloxam, a barrister,
and perfected by the late Lord Grimthorpe.   The
idea was to make the scape wheel, instead of directly
driving the pendulum, lift a weight, which, being
subsequently released, drove the pendulum.   The
consequence was, that inequalities in wind pressure,
which affected the driving force of the scape wheel,
would not act on the pendulum, which would be
always driven by the uniform fall of a fixed and
definite weight.   A movement of this kind has
been fixed in the great clock at Westminster, and
has gone admirably.   A description of its details
will be found in the *Encyclopædia Britannica,*
written by Lord Grimthorpe himself.

All sorts of eccentric clocks and watches have
been proposed.   For instance, it seems wonderful
to see a pair of hands fitted to the centre of a
transparent sheet of glass go round and keep time
with apparently nothing to drive them.

But the mystery is simple.   The seeming sheet
of glass is not one sheet, but four.   The two centre
sheets move round invisibly, carrying the hour
hand and minute hand with them, being urged by

little rollers below on which they rest. When you touch the glass the outside sheets appear at rest, and you do not suspect that it is other than a single sheet. But beware of dust, for if dust gets on the inner plate you detect the trick. In this way a mechanical hand was made that wrote down answers to questions. This plan can be applied to all sorts of tricks.

Sir William Congreve, an ingenious inventor, proposed to make a clock that measured time by letting a ball roll down an incline. When it got to the bottom it hit a lever, which released a spring and tipped the plane up again, so that the ball now ran down the other way. It is a poor time-keeper, and the idea was not original, for a ball had been previously designed for the same purpose.

Sometimes clocks are constructed by attaching pendulums to bronze figures, which have so small a movement that the eye is unable to detect it. The figure appears to be at rest, but is in reality slowly rocking to and fro. It is necessary to make the movement as small as about one four hundredth of an inch in half a second, if the movement is to escape human observation. For a movement of one two hundredth of an inch per second is about the largest that will certainly remain unperceived.

In mediæval times clocks were constructed with all sorts of queer devices. The people of the upper town at Basle having quarrelled with those of the lower town, fought and beat them. To commemorate this victory they put on the old bridge at the upper town a clock provided with an iron head, that slowly put out and drew in a long tongue of derision. This clock may still be seen in the museum. It is as though the council of the city of London put a clock of derision at Temple Bar to put out its tongue at the County Council.

I do not propose here to describe the striking mechanism of clocks. There are several different ways of arranging it. They are rather complicated to follow out, but they all resolve themselves into a few simple principles. As the hour hand revolves it carries a cam so arranged as to be deeper cut away for the twelfth hour, less for the eleventh, and so on. When the minute hand comes to the hour it releases the striking mechanism, which, urged by a weight, begins to revolve, and, driving an arm carrying a pin, raises a hammer, which goes on striking away as the arm revolves. This would continue for ever if it were not that at the same moment an arm is liberated which falls against the cam. At each stroke the arm is (by the striking apparatus) raised a bit back into position. When it comes back into position it stops the striking. It thus acts as a counter, or reckoner of the blows given, stopping the movement when the clock has struck sufficiently. If the counting mechanism fails to act, we have the phenomenon which occasionally occurs of a "Grandfather" clock striking the whole of the hours for the week without stopping.

A chiming clock is simpler still. For here we have a barrel covered with pins, like the barrel in a musical box. As the pins go round they raise hammers which fall against bells. The barrel is wound up and driven by a spring or weight. When the clock comes to the hour, the barrel is released, and rotating, plays the tune.

If you want to make a clock wake you up in the morning it can be done by making the striking arrangement hammer away with no counting mechanism to stop it until the weight has run down. If, not content with that, you want the sheets pulled off the bed or the bed tilted up, or a can of water emptied over the person who will not rise, a mechanical device known as a relay must be used. It is very simple. What is wanted is that, after the lapse of a time which a clock must measure, a considerable force must be exerted to pull off the bedclothes. It would be absurd to make the clock exercise this pull. It is obviously better to attach the clothes by a hook to a rope which passes over a pulley, and from which hangs a weight. A pin secures the weight from falling, the pin being withdrawn by the clock. The work is thus done by the weight when released by the clock.

In like manner, if you have a telegraph designed to print messages at a distance, you do not send along the wires the whole force necessary for doing the printing. You only send impulses, which, like triggers, release the forces by which the letters are to be stamped.

Electric clocks of many kinds have been invented. The principle of an electric escapement is similar to that of an ordinary escapement.

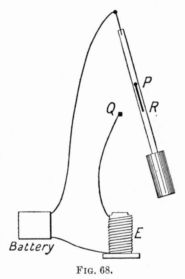

FIG. 68.

The reader no doubt knows that, when a circuit of wire is joined or completed leading to a source of electricity, electricity flows through the wire.

If the wire is wound round a piece of iron, then, whenever the circuit is joined, a current is set in motion, and the iron becomes an electro-magnet. When the circuit is severed the iron ceases to be a magnet.

If put at a proper position it would at each time

an iron pendulum approached give it a small
impulse provided that at that instant the current
is turned on. This can easily be made to be done
by the pendulum itself. For just as the pendulum
is coming back to the central position a flipper P
attached to the rod can be caused to make contact
with a piece of metal fixed on its path. Then the
electro-magnet, becoming magnetised, exerts a pull
on the iron pendulum. On the return beat of the
pendulum the other side of the flipper R strikes
the obstruction. But if that side R is covered with
ebonite or some non-conducting material no current
will be set in motion, and the electro-magnet will
not (as it would otherwise do) retard the pendulum.
Such a pendulum has therefore an impulse given
to it every second beat.

Such pendulums do not act very well, because it
is difficult to keep metallic surfaces like Q clean,
and therefore misses often occur. Besides, the
strength of the current varies with the goodness
of the contact and with other things.

What is now preferred is to make an arrangement by which an electric current winds the clock
up every minute or so. By this means the impulse
which drives the clock is not a varying electric one,
but is a steady weight. The most successful clocks
have been made on these principles.

The advantage of electricity is, that by means of
the current that actuates the clock, or winds it up,

you can at regular intervals set the hands in motion of a great number of clocks.

So that only one going clock with a pendulum is needed. The other clocks distributed over the building have only faces and hands, and a very few simple wheels, to which a slight push is given by an electro-magnet, say, every minute or so. The system is therefore well adapted for offices and hotels.

In America, by means of electric contacts, clocks have been arranged to put gramophones into action. You will remember that it was pointed out that if a wire were dragged over a file a sound would be produced due to the little taps made as the wire clicked against the rough cuts on the file, and that the tone of the note depended on the fineness of the cuts, and hence the rapidity of the little taps. You can imagine that, if the roughnesses were properly arranged, we might get the tones to vary, and thus imitate speech. This is the principle of the gramophone. The roughnesses are produced by a tool, which, vibrating under the influence of human speech, makes small cuts in a soft material. This is hardened, and then, when another wire is dragged over the cuts, the voice is reproduced.

In this way clocks are made to speak and tell the children when dinner is ready and when to go to bed. On this simple plan, too, dolls can be made to speak.

The modern methods of clock and watch-making are very different from those in use in olden days. In former times the pivots were turned up by hand on small lathes, and even the teeth of the wheels were filed out.   Each hole in the clock or watch frame was drilled out separately, and each wheel separately fitted in, so that the watch was gradually built up as one would build a house. Each wheel, of course, only fitted its own watch, and the parts of watches were not interchangeable.

This has now all been altered.   By means of elaborate machinery the whole of the work of cutting out every wheel and the making of every single part is done by tools moved independently of the will of the workman, whose only duty is to sit still and see the things made.   He is, as it were, the slave of the machine, watching it and answering to its calls.   Or shall we rather say that he is the machine's employer and master ?   He has here a servant who never tires nor ever disobeys him.   All the machine requires is that its cutting edges should be exactly true and sharp and microscopically perfect; then it will cut away and make wheel after wheel.   It oils itself.   It only wants the man to act as superintendent, and stop it if any cutting edge gets unduly worn.   For this purpose he measures the work it is doing from time to time with a microscope to see that it is good and true and exact.

When all the parts have thus been made you have perhaps a hundred boxes, each with a thousand watch parts in it, each part exactly like its fellows. You take one wheel or bit from each box indiscriminately, and you then have the materials for a watch, screws, fittings, pins, and all. All you have now got to do is simply to screw them all together, like putting together a puzzle. Everything fits ; there is no snipping or filing.

In such a watch if a bit gets broken you simply send for another bit of the same kind and fit it into its place.

Motor cars, bicycles, and many other machines are, or ought to be, made in this manner, so that if a driver at York breaks a part of the car he simply sends to London for another. It comes and fits into its place at once. But for this sort of plan you must do work true to much less than a thousandth of an inch, and, of course, no one must want to indulge his individual fancy as to the shape or appearance of the watch. The whole advantage consists in dead uniformity. But the cheapness is surprising. You can have a better watch now for 30s. than could have been got for £30 twenty years ago.

Artistic people are in the habit of condemning this uniformity as though it were inartistic and degrading. In truth, it is not degrading to get a machine to do what you want at the expense of as little labour as possible. You pay 30s. for the

watch, but you have £28 10s. left to spend on
pictures.

Only one ought not to confuse industry with art.
Watches made in this way have no pretence to be
artistic products. They are simply useful. To
rule them all over with machine lines or to put
hideous machine ornament on them is purely and
simply base and degrading. Let your *ornament* be
hand work, your utility machine work.

Thus then I have endeavoured to give a
very brief sketch of the modes of measuring
time, and incidentally to introduce my readers to
those laws of motion which are the foundation of
so large a part of modern science.

It only remains that I should shortly describe
modern apparatus by means of which it is possible
to measure with accuracy periods of time so short
as to appear impossible. But when you see how it
is done the method seems easy enough. It is still
by means of a pendulum, only a pendulum beating
time not once, but hundreds and even thousands of
times in a second.

And such pendulums, instead of being difficult
to make, are remarkably simple, and present
no difficulty whatever. For we have only to
use the tuning fork which has been previously
described.

The tuning fork consists of a piece of steel bent
into a U shape. The arms are set vibrating so as

alternately to approach and recede from one another.

The reason why there are two arms is that, if they come together and recede, they balance, and hence the instrument as a whole does not shake on its base. This balance of moving parts of a rapidly moving machine is very important. Some motor cars are arranged so that the engines are "balanced," and the moving parts come in and out simultaneously, leaving the centre of gravity unchanged whatever be the position of the motion. This makes the vibration of the car very small.

The tuning fork is therefore balanced. Being elastic, it obeys Hook's law, "As the force, so the deflection." And therefore, as we have seen, the vibrations of the fork are isochronous.

A fork with arms about six or seven inches long will make about fifty or sixty vibrations in a second. How are we to record those vibrations, and how keep the tuning fork vibrating?

A train of wheels is almost an impossibility, not perhaps so impossible as might be supposed, but still very difficult. So a different method is adopted. A little wire projects from one tuning fork arm. A piece of glazed paper is gently smoked by means of a wax taper, and is stretched round a well-made brass drum. The tuning fork is then put so that the little wire just touches the paper. The tuning fork is then made to vibrate by a blow,

N 2

and while it is vibrating the drum is revolved. Thus a wavy line is formed on the drum by the wire on the tuning fork. If the tuning fork made

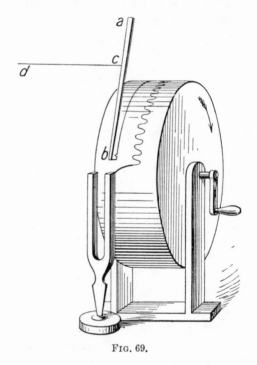

FIG. 69.

fifty complete vibrations to and fro in a second there would be one hundred such indentations, fifty to the right and fifty to the left, and by these the time can be measured as you would measure a length upon a rule.

If an arm a b be fitted to move sideways when
a little string c d is pulled, and be also provided
with a small wire, so as to touch the drum, then it
also will trace a straight line on the drum as the
wire lightly scratches away the thin coating of
smoke. Now, if it is suddenly jerked and flips back,
then a little indentation will be made
in the line, and if when we are to
measure a rapid lapse of time a jerk
is given at the beginning, and another
jerk at the end of it, we should get
a diagram like that in the adjoining
figure, where a is the trace of the tuning
fork, b that of the indicating arm. The
time which has elapsed between the
jerk which produced the indentation c
and that which produced the indentation d will be about three and three-
quarter double indentations of the
tuning fork line, thus indicating three
and three-quarter fiftieths of a second.

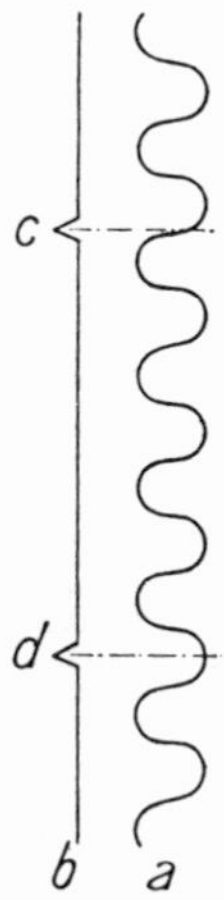

FIG. 70.

It is easy to see how delicate this means of measurement can be made. With small tuning forks we can
easily measure times to a thousandth part of a
second, and much less if desired.

The jerk may be given by electricity if it is
wished. When the current is joined a little electro-
magnet pulls a bit of iron and gives a pull to the
string. So extremely rapid is the flight of electricity

that no appreciable time is lost in its transit through the wires, so that the impulse may be given from a distance. Thus we may arrange that when a cannon ball leaves a gun an electric impulse shall be given. When it reaches and hits a target another electric impulse is given. These make nicks in the tracing line on the drum from which we can easily compute the time that has elapsed between the

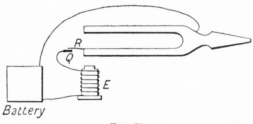

FIG. 71.

leaving of the mouth of the gun and the arrival of the shot at its destination.

Such an apparatus is used in modern gunnery experiments. It is an elaborate one, but is based on the principle above described.

Drums are sometimes driven by clockwork, and tuning forks are also often kept vibrating by electricity, thus constituting very rapidly moving electric clocks. The arrangement is simple. An electromagnet E is put in the vicinity of the arm of the tuning fork. A small piece of wire from the arm is in contact with a piece of metal Q, from which a wire runs to the electro-magnet, thence to a battery, and from the battery to the tuning fork, through which the current runs to the wire R. When the fork vibrates the arm, being bent outwards, makes the wire R touch Q. This at once causes the electro-magnet to give a small pull to the steel arm of the tuning fork, and thus assists the swing of the arm. The whole arrangement is exactly analogous to an electric clock, as may be seen by comparing Fig. 71 with Fig. 68.

There is another method of measuring rapid intervals of time which also merits attention. It is to let a body drop at the commencement of the period of time to be measured, and mark how far it falls in the time, and then find the time from the equation given previously,

$$S = \tfrac{1}{2} g\, t^2.$$

It is practically done by letting a piece of smoked glass fall and making a small pointer make two dots upon it, one at the beginning, another at the end, of the time to be measured.

An interesting adaptation of this method can serve as a basis of a curious toy.

Take a crossbow, with a bolt with a spike on it; fix it firmly in a vice so that the barrel points at a spot a on a wooden wall. On the spot a hang a cardboard figure of a cat on to a nail so contrived that when an electro-magnet acts the nail is pulled aside, and the cat drops. Thus let a be the cat, *b* the loop by which it is hung over the nail *c*, that is fixed to another piece of iron furnished with a hinge at *c*, so that when the electric current is turned on the nail *c* is withdrawn and the cat drops. Carry the wires from the electro-magnet and battery to the crossbow, and so arrange them that when the bolt leaves the muzzle one is pressed against the other, and contact made.

Now here you have an apparatus such that exactly

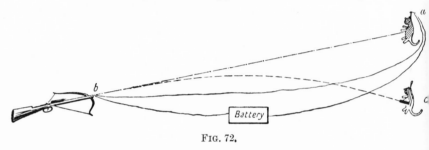

FIG. 72.

as the bolt leaves the crossbow, the cat drops. Now what will happen?

When the bolt leaves the bow it is subject to two motions, one a motion of projection at a uniform pace in the direction of *b a* from the bow to the target.

But it is also subject to another force, namely that of gravity, which acts on it vertically, and deflects it *in a vertical direction* exactly as much and as fast as a body would do if dropped from rest at the same instant as the bolt leaves the bow. But

the cat is such a body. Hence, then, since by the
electric arrangement they are both let go together,
they will both drop simultaneously, and thus will
always be on the same level, and when the bolt
reaches the wooden wall and has fallen vertically
from a to c, the cat will also have fallen vertically
from a to c, and the bolt will pin him to the wall.

It does not matter how far you
take the bow from the wall, nor
how strong the bow is, nor how
heavy the bolt is, nor how heavy
the cat is, nor whether $a\,b$ is
horizontal or pointing upwards
or downwards.

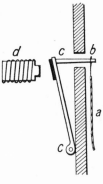

In every case, if only the
barrel is pointed directly at the
cat, then the bolt and cat fall
simultaneously and at the same
rate, and the bolt will pin
the cat to the wall.

FIG. 73.

In trying the experiment the bolt should be pretty
heavy, say half a pound, and have a good spike; but
if carefully done the experiment will succeed every
time. It enables you also to measure the speed of
flight of the bolt. For if the distance of the bow
from the wall be thirty feet, and the cat have fallen
three feet when it is struck, then the time of fall is

$$T^2 = \sqrt{\frac{2\,S}{g}} = \sqrt{\frac{6}{g}} = \cdot 43 \text{ seconds.} \quad \text{But the bolt in}$$

this time went thirty feet; hence its velocity was thirty feet in ·43 seconds, or seventy feet per second.

Of course if you make the bolt heavier the velocity of projection will become slower, the time longer, and hence the cat will fall further before it is transfixed by the bolt.

My task is now at a close. I have endeavoured not merely to give a description of clocks and various apparatus for measuring time, but to explain the fundamental principles of mechanics which lie at the root of the subject.

May I end with a word of advice to parents ?

There is a certain number of boys, but only a certain number, who have a real love for mechanical science. Such boys should be encouraged in every way by the possession of tools and apparatus, but in the selection of this apparatus the following principles should be borne in mind :—

First, that almost everything a boy wants can be made with wood, and metal, and wire, and string, *if* he has someone to give him a little instruction how to do it. A bent bit of steel jammed in a vice makes an excellent tuning fork.

Second, that he wants not toy tools, but good tools. If an expert wants a good tool, how much more a beginner.

Third, that he ought to have a reasonably dry and comfortable place to work in, and the help and advice of the village carpenter or blacksmith.

Fourth, that he ought not to be allowed to potter with his tools, but to make something really sensible and useful, and not begin a dozen things and finish none.

Fifth, that the making of apparatus to show scientific facts is more useful than making bootjacks for his father or workboxes for his mother.

And, *lastly*, that a little money spent in this way will keep many a young rascal from worrying his sisters and stoning the cat; and when the inevitable time comes at which he must face the young man's first trial, THE EXAMINER, he will often thank his stars that he learned in play the fundamental formula $S = \frac{1}{2} g t^2$, and that he knows the nature of " harmonic motion," the two most important principles in the measurement of time.

THE END.

APPENDIX ON THE SHAPE OF THE TEETH OF WHEELS.

The teeth of wheels for watches and clocks need particular care in shaping, and it may be of interest if I describe briefly the principles upon which these wheels are made.   What is required is that the motion shall not be communicated by jerks as the teeth successively engage one another, but that the

motion shall be perfectly smooth. The problem
therefore becomes this: How are we to arrange the
teeth of the wheels so that as one of them turns
and drives the other round the leverage or turning
power exercised by the driving wheel on the driven
wheel shall always be uniform? Now if the teeth
were simple spikes one can easily see that this
would not be the case. For instance, as the arm $a\,c$

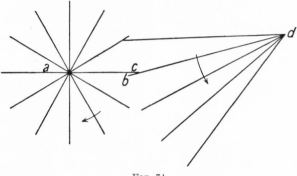

FIG. 74.

turned round, driving before it the arm $b\,d$, the
point c would scrape along, and the leverage between
the two teeth would constantly alter. Evidently
some other construction must be adopted. Before
we can determine what it is to be, we must inquire
what the leverage would be between two rods, $a\,c$
and $d\,b$, mounted on pivots at a and d. The answer
to this question is, that when a lever such as $a\,c$
presses with its end against another, $d\,b$, the power

is exercised in a direction $c\,g$ at right angles to $d\,b$.
Hence the leverage between the two arms is in the
ratio of $a\,e$ to $d\,c$. The system is just as if we had

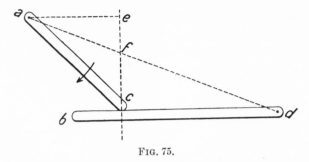

FIG. 75.

a lever $a\,e$ united to a lever $d\,c$ by a rigid rod $e\,c$ at
right angles to both of them.

Whence then the ratio of the power is as $a\,e$ is to $d\,c$.

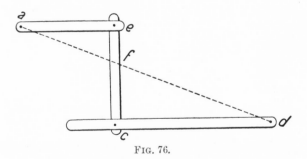

FIG. 76.

But since the triangles $a\,e\,f$, $d\,c\,f$, are similar,
$a\,e$ is to $d\,c$ as $a\,f$ to $f\,d$. Whence then we get this
general proposition: If one body mounted on an

axis is pressing upon another body mounted on an
axis, the pressure exerted between them is always
exercised in a direction, shown by the dotted line,

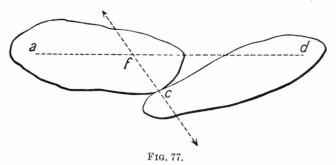

FIG. 77.

at right angles to the two surfaces in contact; and
the ratio of the leverage is found by drawing a line
from one axis to the other, so as to cut the line of

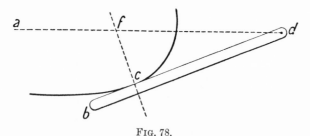

FIG. 78.

direction of pressure in f. The leverage of one on
the other is then as af to fd. Our problem has
now become the following: Given a rod $b\,d$, suppose
that it is pressed upon by a curved surface mounted
on an axis at a. Then the direction of the pressure

that the curved surface (called in engineering language a cam) will exercise on the rod $b\,d$ is shown by the dotted line ; and the ratio of the driving power to the driven power is as df to af. Now how can we shape the cam so that as it moves round, and different parts of its surface come successively into contact with $b\,c$, the ratio of the leverage is always the

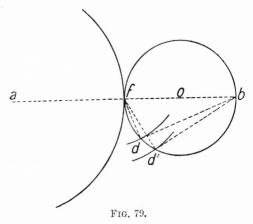

FIG. 79.

same; that is to say, the ratio of af to fd shall always be constant ; that is to say, the line drawn through the point of contact perpendicular to the curve at that point, shall always pass through the point f?

Evidently, if this is to be so, the point d must be on a semicircle, whose diameter is $f\,b$, for in that case the angle $f\,d\,b$ will always be a right angle.

The surface must then be so arranged that, whatever be the position of the cam and of the rod $b\,d$, the point of contact between them must always be on the semicircle $f\,c\,d$; that is to say, as the cam moves round the axis a its shape must be such that a line drawn from f to the point where it cuts the circle $f\,d\,b$ is always perpendicular to the curve.

Now suppose that we move a circle whose centre is at a, and radius $a\,f$, so as to roll the circle $f\,d\,b$ by simple surface friction round its centre o, then any point d on it would mark out a curve on a piece of

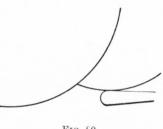

FIG. 80.

paper attached to the moving circle whose centre is at a, and the direction of motion of the curve would always be such that the point d on it would at any instant be describing a circle round f, and the direction of the curve would thus at any point always be at right angles to the line $d\,f$ for the time being.

This curve, caused by the rolling of one circle on another, is called an epicycloid. Hence, then, for a clock, if we make the pinion wheel with straight spokes and the driving wheel with its teeth cut in the form of epicycloids, caused by rolling a circle with a diameter equal to the radius of the pinion upon the driving wheel, we shall get a uniform ratio of leverage one upon the other.

The circles with radii af, bf, are called the "pitch circles," and these radii are in the ratio of the movement that is required for the wheels, usually six to one or eight to one, as the case may be. The sides of the teeth of the pinion wheels are straight lines radiating from the centre, and rounded off at the ends so as to avoid accidental jambing. The teeth of the cogwheel have epicycloidal sides. The tips are cut off so as to be out of the way, and spaces are left between them for the width of the leaves of the pinion wheel.

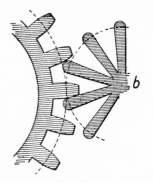

FIG. 81.

Both pinion wheels and cog-wheels are cut by cutters rotating at a high speed, about 3,500 times in a minute, the cutters being carefully shaped for the pinion wheels with straight edges, for the cog-wheels in epicycloids. It is a pretty thing to see a wheel-cutting engine at work, the cutter flying round with a hum, cutting the rim of a brass wheel into teeth, the brass coming off in flakes thinner than fine hairs and falling in fine dust. When a tooth is cut, the wheel is moved round one division of an apparatus called a "dividing plate," so as to present a new part of the wheel to the cutter. Of course,

T.C.   O

the cutter and wheels must all be properly proportioned. Cutters are sold in sets duly shaped
for the work they have to do. Wheel-cutting is a
special branch of the clockmaking industry. The
reason the speed of cutting is so high is because it
is desired to take off small portions of metal at a
time, and thus not strain the wheel and the cutting
machinery. If bigger cuts were made, then the
machine would have to go slower, for it is a
principle in the construction of cutting machinery
that the speed of the cut must always be proportioned to the depth of it. If you want to take deep
cuts you must move the cutting edge slowly, and
vice versâ. The most modern method of making
cogwheels of brass, and the best, is to stamp them
out of solid sheet metal at a single punch of a
punching machine, and cheap watches are always
made in this way. In fact, the whole method of
watch and clock-making is undergoing a trans-
formation.

Before the time of the great engineering develop-
ment which took place towards the end of the
eighteenth century, the making of machines was
a sort of fine art. Cogwheels were cut by hand.
The circumference was marked out by means of
compasses. Then holes were drilled round the
rim, and teeth cut out leading into them, and
shaped by means of special files constructed for the
purpose (Fig. 82). Big machinery was all shaped out

at the forge and by the file. The engineers com-
plained that you could not get big work made true
even to the eighth of an inch. But watches and
clocks were beautifully made, though only at the
cost of hours of patient measuring and filing. The
taste for ornament still existed. The wheels and
backs of watches were chased over with the most
beautiful patterns; the frames of the clocks were
wrought into beautiful figures and forms. Even
astronomical instruments were embellished.

Then came the era of severe accuracy. Men of
science took the government
of machine - making whose
feelings were repugnant to
art in any form. They hated
to see any effort expended in

FIG. 82.

ornament. With severely utilitarian aims, they
banished all appearance of beauty from instruments
and tools of all sorts, so that our modern machines,
from a steam engine down to a watch, are now
models of precise but perfectly unornamented work-
manship. They are the fitting implements of a nation
that wears trousers and tall hats. One has only to
compare an old vessel of war, with its sculptured
prow and streamers, with a modern ironclad to take
note of the difference. The art of ornamentation
is now little more than a spasmodic imitation of
the past, with a historical interest only. As a
living entity it has almost ceased to exist.

But in precision of manufacture the present age is without a rival in the history of the world. People believe no longer in the old methods of scraping and filing, and hand-work directly exercised on metal is rapidly falling into desuetude. It is possible, of course, with a file and scraper and days of labour to get two flat surfaces of metal so perfect that when put together one will lift the other like a sucker on a stone, but it is waste labour. A small machine will do it as well in a few minutes. No longer is a watch built up as one would build a house, fitting part to part. By expensive machines thousands of watch parts are stamped and cut out to pattern, and then a watch is made by taking one of each indiscriminately and just putting them into their places. Comparatively unskilled workmen can do this. Where the skill is wanted is to design and make the machinery and watch the cutters, measuring them with microscopic gauges from time to time, and at once remedying them if an edge is found to be a ten-thousandth part of an inch out of place. So that the labour of man is becoming more and more a labour of design and of supervision. Machines are the slaves that do the work, for in a good machine we have an eye and an arm that never tires, and only needs to be kept in working order. But machines are not artistic, and thus art is lost while precision is gained. At present a desperate attempt is being made to supply by means of machinery the craving of the human mind for art. But it is destined to failure. Art of this kind is generally produced by the same brain that designs machines, and therefore presents an appearance of rigid accuracy and uniformity, which, while essential to an engine, is out of place in an artistic product.

The great manufacturers of our Midlands do not seem to understand that there is no object in making a towel-horse as geometrically accurate as a turning lathe. It will apparently be years before they learn to put art and precision each in the place where it is wanted—precision in the works of the watch, art in the face and the case of it; machine work in the inside of a watch, hand work on the outside. When the public taste is educated so as to see the odious character of the jumble of Gothic, Egyptian, and meaningless ornament on such an article as the case of an American organ, one step will have been made towards the revival of artistic taste.

But to propose as a means of reviving art that we should discontinue the use of machinery or abandon our modern cutters of precision to go back to a hack-saw and file is ridiculous, and could only be suggested by men quite destitute of scientific ideas. Art and precision each has its place: there is room for both ; let neither intrude on the domain of the other.

INDEX.